BMC AUTOBOOK TWO

A Workshop Manual for the
Austin A30, A35, A40 Farina, Austin Healey,
Sprite and MG Midget from 1951 onwards
of 803cc, 948cc and 1098cc including van
and estate versions

by

Kenneth Ball
G I Mech E

AUTOPRESS LTD
Bennett Road Brighton Sussex

Books by the same author :

SWORD REPORT
BMC AUTOBOOK THREE
MINOR AUTOBOOK ONE
VIVA AUTOBOOK ONE

CONTENTS

First Edition   January 1967

Printed in England by
G. Beard & Son
Brighton

ACKNOWLEDGMENT

My thanks are due to The British Motor Corporation Ltd for their unstinted co-operation in supplying data and illustrations.

I am also grateful to a considerable number of owners who have discussed their cars at length and many of whose suggestions have been included in this manual.

INTRODUCTION

This Manual is intended for enthusiasts who have a general knowledge of over-hauling techniques, who are proficient with tools and have access to a reasonably well equipped workshop. Comprehensive instructions are given on all dismantling and overhauling operations where these can be carried out in the above mentioned circumstances. Certain assemblies however require the use of expensive special tools the purchase of which would be unjustified. In these cases certain information is included for the reader's interest but he is recommended to hand the unit to an accredited BMC dealer for attention. Whilst every care has been taken to ensure correctness of information it is obviously not possible to guarantee complete freedom from errors.

All the cars in this manual use the 'A' series BMC engine and as externally they appear identical it is necessary to check the engine prefix number to determine the exact variation. All engines with the prefix 8 are of 803cc, prefix 9 indicates 948cc and prefix 10 is 1098cc.

The 803cc engine was introduced in October 1951 in the A30 and became 948cc in the A35 in September 1956.

In 1958 the Sprite I and the A40 Farina I were announced using this 948cc engine, and in 1961 the MG Midget I was announced, again with this engine.

In the autumn of 1962 the 1098cc version was announced first in the A40 Farina II and then in the Sprite II and Midget I. The Sprite III and Midget II introduced in March 1964 still use the 1098cc engine but these have larger main bearings. This latest version produces 59 bhp at 5500 rpm thus proving the soundness of the basic design which produced 28bhp at 4800 rpm when fitted in the A30.

CHAPTER 1

THE ENGINE

Engine type   Overhauling   Removing from car   Dismantling   Head and valve gear
Camshaft   Sump   Connecting rods and pistons   Crankshaft   Oil pump   Reassembly
Replacing timing gear   Replacing pistons   Replacing the head   Rocker adjustment
Valve timing   Distributor drive   Manifolds, water pump and generator   Fault diagnosis
Modifications

There are three engine sizes covered by this manual, the cubic capacities being 800 cc, 948 cc and 1098 cc respectively. As the basic design of the engines is virtually identical, any instructions for working on one of them will hold for the other two. Those differences which affect overhaul or tuning will be covered by a reference to the particular car concerned. The following table shows that the bore and stroke is the same for each common engine capacity, the extra power for the sports cars coming from an increase in the compression ratio, from the use of two carburetters and modifications to the valve and ignition timings.

	Capacity (cc)	Bore (mm)	Stroke (mm)	Comp. ratio
A30	800	58	76.2	7.2:1
A35 (early)	948	62.94	76.2	7.2:1 and 8.3:1
A35 (later)	1098	64.58	83.72	7.5:1
A40 Mk I, A40 Mk II (early)	948	62.94	76.2	7.2:1 and 8.3:1
A40 Mk II (later)	1098	64.58	83.72	7.5:1 and 8.5:1
'Sprite' Mk I	948	62.94	76.2	8.3:1
'Sprite' Mk II (early) and 'Midget' Mk I (early)	948	62.94	76.2	8.3:1 and 9:1
'Sprite' Mk II (later) and Mk III, 'Midget' Mk I (later) and Mk II ...	1098	64.58	83.72	8.1:1 and 8.9:1

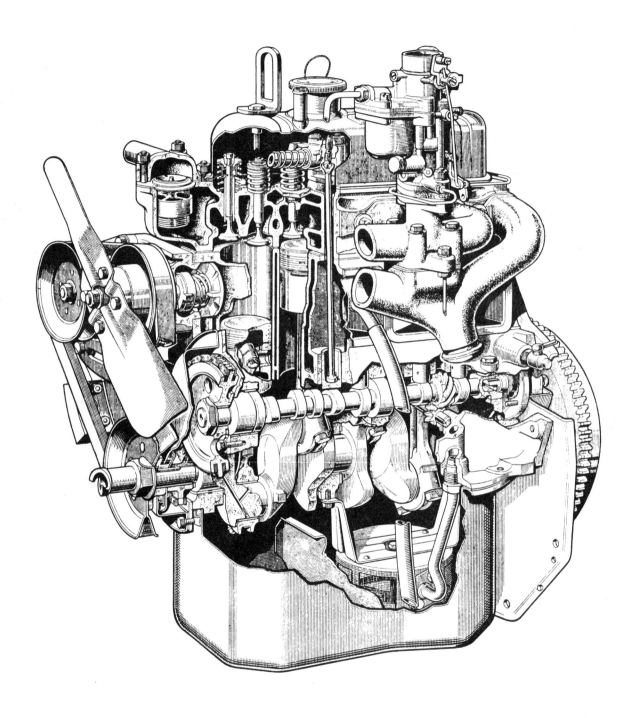

Fig 1:1   Cut-away view of the 948 cc engine. The other engines are basically similar

Engine type

This four cylinder in-line engine has push-rod operated overhead valves working vertically in a detachable head of cast-iron. These can be seen in **FIG 1:1**, where all the salient features which are mentioned can be readily identified. The valves have renewable guides and the stems are fitted with oil seals. The push-rods operate from tappets which are lifted by a chain-driven camshaft on the left-hand side of the engine. The camshaft has three bearings. On some engines the front one has a steel-backed white-metalled liner, the other two running direct in the cast-iron of the cylinder block. On all the 1098 cc engines and on the 948 cc engine fitted to the 'Sprite' II and 'Midget' I, the three bearings all have steel-backed white-metalled liners. The single-roller chain which drives the camshaft is ingeniously tensioned and silenced by two synthetic rubber rings, one on each side of the large chain wheel sprocket teeth. End thrust on the camshaft is taken by a plate bolted to the front of the cylinder block. An integral skew gear to the rear of the camshaft drives a transverse shaft which in turn drives a distributor on the right-hand side of the engine. There is also an eccentric on the camshaft for operating a mechanical fuel pump, if this type of pump is fitted.

The forged steel crankshaft runs in three bearings. These bearings have renewable shells with surfaces of different alloys, selected to suit the loads imposed by varying power outputs. End float is restricted by thrust washers on each side of the centre main bearing. The connecting-rods have big-ends which are split diagonally so that they will pass upwards through the bores. The caps have machined lugs and dowel bolts for accurate location. The big-ends have renewable bearing shells, and like the main bearings these have different alloy surfaces to cope with the various power outputs.

The earlier cars have split-skirt pistons and gudgeon pins clamped in the small-ends of the connecting-rods. Later cars have solid-skirted pistons with fully-floating gudgeon pins which are located endwise in the bosses by spring circlips. Four piston rings are fitted, the top three for compression sealing and the bottom one for oil control.

The oil pump is bolted to the back of the cylinder block and has a slotted shaft which engages a driving pin in the end of the camshaft. Of the two types which can be dismantled, the Burman has sliding vanes in a slotted rotor, while the Hobourn-Eaton pump has inner and outer rotors with specially shaped lobes. Oil reaches the pump from a strainer in the sump, and then goes under pressure to a relief valve on the right-hand side of the engine. This valve restricts oil pressure to a safe maximum when the oil is cold and thick, returning any overflow back to the sump. The oil then proceeds to a gallery along the right-hand side of the engine where, at the rear end, will be found an oil gauge union, or an electrical pressure-operated switch connected to a warning light on the dash. Above this fitting is a banjo union with an external pipe leading to a full-flow oil filter just forward of the starter motor. This contains a felt element which cleans the oil and passes it on to the main gallery to supply the bearings. If the element becomes clogged with dirt, a relief valve in the filter opens to allow unfiltered oil to by-pass the element and go straight to the bearings. On the early engines, the same position is occupied by a throw-away type of by-pass filter. This takes a small quantity of oil from the main stream, cleans it

thoroughly and passes it back to the sump. Branching off the main oil gallery are passages which take oil to the main, big-end and camshaft bearings. From the front camshaft bearing oil passes at reduced pressure to the overhead rocker gear and the timing chain. Draining down the push-rod tubes it then lubricates the tappets and cams.

Overhauling

First, there are a few points to mention which may be helpful. Reference to the right- or left-hand side of the car means that it is viewed as from the driving seat looking forward. No. 1 cylinder is at the front end of the engine. Perfect cleanliness is essential when reassembling. Lubricate all working parts with clean engine oil unless otherwise specified. Exceptions could be, for example, where self-lubricating bushes are used, or where excessive oil would be a nuisance.

If dirty paraffin or petrol is used for cleaning, rinse the parts afterwards in clean petrol and allow to dry. In any case, do not dry them with a fluffy rag. After scraping away all traces of old gaskets and jointing compound, examine the joint faces for burrs. These often cause persistent oil leakage, and a light stroke with a fine file held flat will quickly reveal the high spots without removing metal from the joint face. Always use new split-pins and locking tab washers. Finally, mark everything to ensure that it is replaced in its precise location, but not so heavily that working surfaces are damaged. For example, a light scratch across the two edges of a flanged joint before it is dismantled will make it easy to settle upon the correct position for reassembly.

The BMC engine is so well known for accessibility that tuning or dismantling is readily carried out, either in or out of the car. Neither is it difficult to remove the engine with adequate lifting tackle, the gearbox either coming out with the engine or staying in the chassis. In the case of the A30 and A35 the engine should be removed from below, for all the other models it should be removed upwards.

Taking out the engine and gearbox complete

The following is the general procedure. Where it differs on some models the points will be covered separately.

1 Detach the bonnet from its hinges.
2 Drain the oil and cooling systems.
3 Unclip the radiator and heater hoses (if fitted), and remove the radiator by unscrewing the four fixing bolts from the side flanges.
4 Disconnect the battery positive lead.
5 Remove the sparking plugs, and the distributor cap with leads.
6 Lift off the aircleaner and disconnect all electrical leads, earthing straps, carburetter controls and fuel pipes.
7 Unclamp the exhaust pipe from the manifold and remove the stay to the bell-housing, if a stay is fitted.
8 Remove the hydraulic slave cylinder from the clutch housing and unscrew the speedometer cable from the gearbox.
9 Working inside the car, remove the gearbox cover plate and lift out the gear lever, taking care of the thrust button and spring and the anti-rattle plunger and spring if fitted.
10 Disconnect the propeller shaft at the rear axle end and withdraw it backwards from the gearbox.

11 Support the gearbox on a trolley jack and remove the cross-member.

12 Remove the nuts holding the front mounting rubbers to the engine bracket. Lift the engine slightly and remove the mounting brackets from the car frame.

13 The engine and gearbox can now be lifted forward and up.

Variations of the above procedure are as follows:

On the A30 and A35

1 Release the clutch pedal pull-off spring, and remove the nut, lock-nut and washers from the front end of the operating rod. Release the pedal shaft support flanges, remove the pin from the spherical bush and slide the shaft free from the gearbox.

2 On A30 cars remove the two set screws from the clamping plate under the gearbox rear cover. On A35 cars take out the two set screws passing through the transmission tunnel from inside the car. From below remove the nuts securing the cross-member.

3 Lower the engine and gearbox on to a trolley after checking that all wires and controls have been detached.

4 Lift the front of the car on blocks until the engine and gearbox can be pulled out forwards.

On the A40

1 Remove the battery.

2 Remove the cross-member under the gearbox by taking out two set screws from inside the car and two from below.

3 Arrange slings so that the engine will take up an almost vertical attitude when lifted. It will then clear the front cross-member. Follow the upward and forward motion with a trolley jack under the gearbox.

On the 'Sprite' I

1 If a tachometer is fitted disconnect the drive complete with cable from the rear of the generator.

2 Remove the distributor, and the starter.

3 Remove four self-tapping screws from the gear lever aperture cover. Take off the cover and proceed as on the A30 and A35.

4 The front engine mounting brackets need not be disturbed.

5 Lift the engine, gearbox and propeller shaft forward and up.

Important

Do not detach the propeller shaft from the gearbox. Always remove and replace the engine, gearbox and propeller shaft as a unit.

On the 'Sprites' II and III, and the 'Midgets' I and II

Carry out the same operations as on the 'Sprite' I but:

1 The propeller shaft can be withdrawn over the rear axle on the left-hand side.

Leaving the gearbox behind on all models

1 Do not drain the gearbox.

2 Take the weight of the gearbox on a jack and remove all the set screws and bolts from the bell-housing flange. Pull the engine horizontally forward until the gearbox first-motion shaft is clear, and then proceed to remove the engine.

On all the 'Sprites' and 'Midgets' the starter must be removed, and also the filter casing, with the exception of 'Sprite' I.

Separating the engine from the gearbox when they are out of the car

Remove all the bolts and set screws holding the bell-housing to the cylinder block and rear engine mounting plate. With the gearbox fully supported so that it cannot hang on the first-motion shaft, the units are drawn apart.

Dismantling the engine

It would be useful at this stage to point out that many of the following sequences can be adopted with the engine still in the car. For instance, with the head off and the sump removed, the big-ends can be split and the pistons with the connecting-rods pushed upwards out of the bores. The tappets can be removed through the engine side-covers. With the radiator off, the water pump and the timing gear can receive attention. For the other major operations it is best to work with the engine out of the car. The inlet and exhaust manifolds can be removed as a unit complete with the carburetter if desired. The manifold assembly is attached to the head by six studs, nuts and washers, the four large inner washers bridging both inlet and exhaust flanges. The hot-spot can be separated by unscrewing the four long screws in the middle. Renew the gasket between the joint faces if it is damaged. Leave these screws finger-tight until the manifold nuts are tightened fully. If the manifold gasket is replaced with a new one, fit it with the perforated metal face to the manifold.

The head, valves and rocker gear

FIG 1 : 2 shows these parts in exploded form. To take off the head, slacken the holding-down nuts a little at a time to avoid distortion. If the engine is in the car, do not attempt to remove the head until the water system has been drained. There are nine holding-down nuts to be taken off. The small nuts on top of the right-hand side of the rocker pedestals do not prevent the head from lifting, but if the valves are to be removed then the rocker gear can also be released. If the head sticks, do not drive a screwdriver between the joint faces, but tap the sides of the head with light hammer blows on a piece of wood. Alternatively, the sparking plugs can be replaced and the engine turned over, when the head should free itself.

If decarbonising is necessary, do most of the scraping with the valves still in place so that the seats are not damaged. The valves have 45-degree faces and a single spring normally, but the sports cars have double springs. Inside the spring is a shroud and an oil-sealing ring of synthetic rubber. To remove the valves pull off the hairpin circlip round the cotters and compress the spring with a suitable tool. The cotters can then be removed and the spring released. The cap, oil-sealing ring and the shroud can be separated from the spring, which should then be checked for length to see if a replacement is needed.

Examine the valve seats and the seatings in the head for wear and deep pitting. The valves can be re-ground by a garage, and a well-equipped garage can also machine away badly worn seats in the head and fit inserts if necessary. Worn valve guides can be pressed out and then replaced by driving in new ones until $\frac{19}{32}$ in projects from the machined valve spring face as shown in FIG 1:3. The seats must then be re-cut to ensure that they are con-

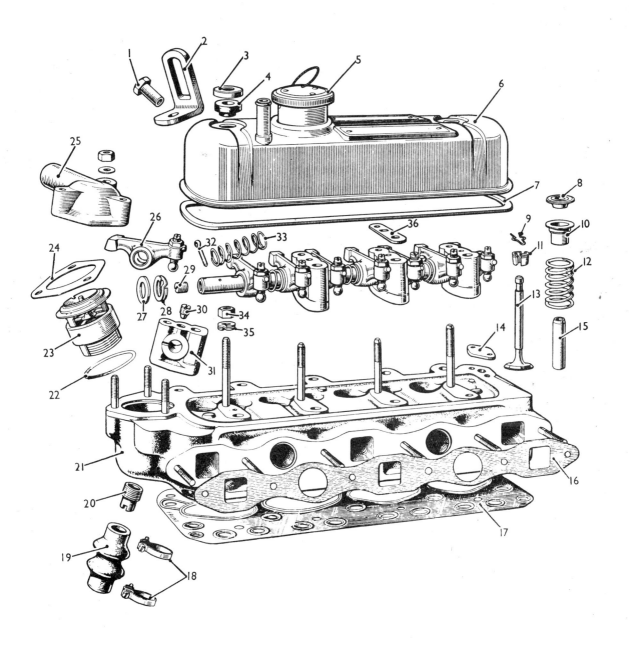

Fig 1:2 The cylinder head components

Key to Fig 1:2   1 Valve rocker cover cap nut.   2 Engine sling bracket.   3 Cup washer.   4 Rubber bush.   5 Oil filler cap.
6.Valve rocker cover.   7 Rocker cover joint washer.   8 Valve spring cap.   9 Valve cotter circlip.   10 Valve oil seal retainer.
11 Valve cotters.   12 Valve spring.   13 Valve.   14 Cover plate.   15 Valve guide.   16 Joint washer.   17 Gasket.
18 Hose clips.   19 By-pass hose.   20 By-pass tube.   21 Cylinder head.   22 Thermostat joint washer.   23 Thermostat.
24 Water outlet elbow joint washer.   25 Water outlet elbow.   26 Rocker.   27 Plain washer.   28 Spring washer.
29 Rocker shaft plug.   30 Locating grub screw.   31 Rocker shaft pedestal.   32 Split pin.   33 Rocker spacing spring.
34 Rocker bracket nut.   35 Rocker bracket washer.   36 Rocker bracket plate.

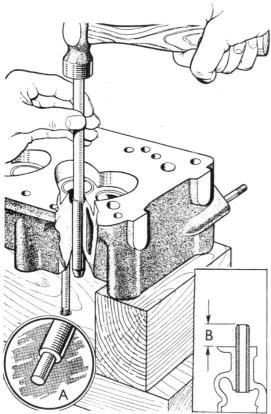

Fig 1:3 Using the stepped drift (A) to remove a valve guide. (B) shows the projection above the top face

centric with the guide bores. The valves can be ground in with a rubber suction tool. When reassembling springs on earlier engines, fit the oil-sealing ring with its chamfered face downwards in the shroud. Later engines have the assembly shown in **FIG 1:4** where a ring of circular section can be seen. This must be pressed over the valve stem until it reaches the bottom of the cotter recess. Both types of ring are easier to fit if they are soaked in clean engine oil for a short time. It is most important to fit new sealing rings at every overhaul or oil-sealing may suffer.

To strip the rocker gear, unscrew the locating grub screw from the top of the front pedestal. Note that this pedestal is drilled for lubricating oil which passes into the hollow rocker shaft and thence to the rockers. Remove the split pin, plain washer and spring washer from the front end of the shaft, when all the rockers, spacing springs and pedestals can be drawn off, taking care to mark them for correct reassembly. All the parts can be seen in **FIG 1:2**, which also shows the locking plate for the locating grub screw. There may be one of these on top of each pedestal on later engines, but it is possible that there may be one only on the front pedestal. The rocker shaft can be cleaned internally by removing the screwed plug from the end. The rockers, which are bushed, may be forgings, or made of steel pressings. These cannot be mixed in one assembly, but a complete set of pressed steel ones can be substituted for forgings and vice versa. In addition, the bushes in the

pressed steel rockers cannot be replaced. When re-assembling, start with the front pedestal, securing it with the locating grub screw. The rocker shaft should have the screwed plug in the end towards the front of the head. Tightening the pedestal nuts will also clamp the rocker shaft.

Important

To remove the rocker assembly with the head remaining on the cylinder block it is necessary to drain the radiator and slacken all the cylinder head securing nuts, because four of the rocker shaft pedestal nuts also secure the head. Failure to slacken the five external cylinder head nuts may result in distortion of the head, with subsequent water leakage.

With the rocker gear out of the way, the push-rods can be lifted out, storing them in the correct order for replacement. Their stems should be straight and the ends examined for wear. At the bottom, the ball-end locates in a barrel tappet. These can be removed by turning the camshaft until each rising tappet can be lifted out, keeping these in the correct order too. They can be seen in **FIG 1:5**, being actually located inside the side covers. New tappets are fitted by selective assembly so that they just fall into their guides under their own weight.

The valve timing gear

To dismantle the timing chain and chain wheels, and to remove the camshaft, proceed as follows. **FIGS 1:5** and **1:6** will enable the parts to be identified. First slacken the generator bolts and remove the belt. Flatten the locking plate under the starting dog, unscrew the dog and prise off the pulley. The timing cover is secured by four large and six small set screws, each fitted with a spring and a plain washer. Where the fan pulley boss passes through the cover, there is an oil seal either of felt or of synthetic rubber with lips. If there has been leakage at this point renew the seals. If the timing cover is being replaced after a new seal has been fitted, it is best done, in the case of the rubber seal, by filling the lips with grease. The fan pulley hub should be lubricated and the boss pushed and turned

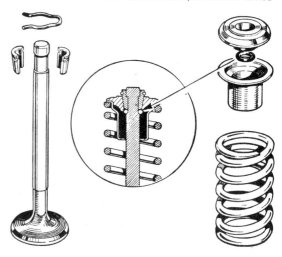

Fig 1:4 Valve assembly showing correct position for oil sealing ring

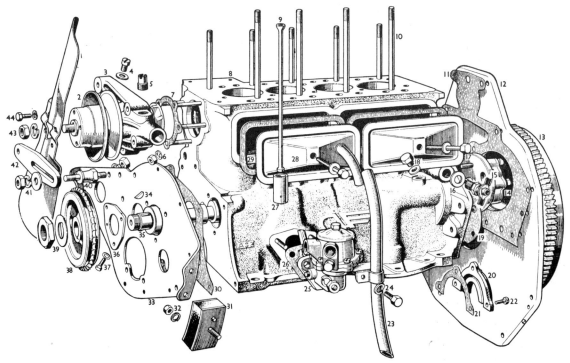

Fig 1:5   An exploded view of the crankcase assembly

Key to Fig 1:5   1 Fan blade.   2 Water pump pulley.   3 Water pump.   4 Water pump screwed plug and washer.
5 Water pump by-pass tube.   6 Nut and washer for water pump stud.   7 Water pump joint washer.   8 Cylinder block.
9 Push rod.   10 Cylinder head studs in block.   11 Rear mounting plate joint washer.   12 Rear mounting plate.
13 Flywheel and starter ring.   14 Oil pump.   15 Cylinder block drain tap.   16 Washer for drain tap.
17 Setscrew and washer for side cover.   18 Oil priming plug and joint washer.   19 Oil pump joint washer.   20 Crankcase rear cover.
21 Joint washer for rear cover.   22 Rear cover setscrew.   23 Crankcase vent pipe.   24 Setscrew and washer.   25 Petrol pump.
26 Petrol pump joint washer.   27 Tappet.   28 Cylinder side cover, front.   29 Joint washer for side cover.
30 Front mounting plate joint washer.   31 Rubber mounting.   32 Nut and washer for rubber mounting.
33 Engine front mounting plate.   34 Woodruff key.   35 Camshaft.   36 Camshaft locating plate.
37 Setscrew and shakeproof washer.   38 Camshaft gear and tensioner rings.   39 Nut and lockwasher.
40 Pillar for adjusting link.   41 Nut and washers for link.   42 Dynamo adjusting link.   43 Nut and washer for pulley.
44 Setscrew and washer for fan blade.

gently until it enters the seal. The timing cover, with the
pulley left in place, is then fed on to the crankshaft with
the keyway and key in line. After this the cover can be
carefully turned until the securing bolt holes are lined up.

With the timing cover off, the next item to be found on
the crankshaft is a dished oil thrower which must always
be replaced with the concave side facing forwards. To
dismantle the chain drive unlock and remove the camshaft
chain wheel nut and lock washer. Now ease both chain
wheels forward a little at a time with small levers. After
removing both wheels and chain make a careful note of
the packing washers which are on the crankshaft immediately behind the crankshaft sprocket. If new camshaft or
crankshaft components have been fitted, check the alignment of the two chain wheels on reassembly. This is done
by placing a straight-edge across the sides of the camshaft wheel teeth and measuring the gap between the
crankshaft chain wheel and the straight-edge with a feeler
gauge. This measurement will be the thickness of the
packing washers required behind the crankshaft wheel,
see **FIG 1:7**. There is a synthetic rubber ring on each side
of the camshaft wheel for the purpose of tensioning and

silencing the chain. If these are worn or the chain is noisy
replace with new rings.

Removing the camshaft

1 Disconnect the vacuum pipe and low-tension lead from
   the distributor.
2 Take out the two bolts and flat washers securing the
   distributor to its housing. Do not slacken the clamping
   plate bolt or the ignition timing will be lost. Now withdraw the distributor.
3 Unscrew the third bolt and remove the distributor
   housing.
4 Screw a tappet cover securing bolt, or any suitable rod
   with a $\frac{5}{16}$ in UNF thread, into the end of the distributor
   drive spindle and withdraw it as shown in **FIG 1:8**.
5 Behind the camshaft chain wheel is a triangular plate
   secured to the cylinder block by three set screws and
   shakeproof washers. By removing this and the mechanical fuel pump if one is fitted, the camshaft can be
   withdrawn.
   The triangular plate controls the end float of the camshaft. If this exceeds the figure given in the Technical Data

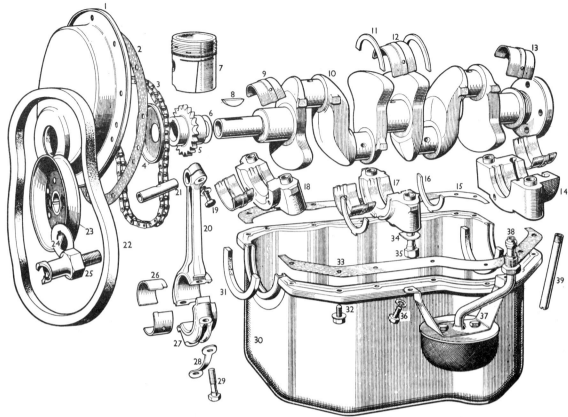

Fig 1:6 The crankshaft and sump assembly

Key to Fig 1:6 1 Engine front cover. 2 Joint washer for cover. 3 Timing chain. 4 Crankshaft oil thrower. 5 Crankshaft gear. 6 Packing washers. 7 Piston. 8 Woodruff key. 9 Front main half bearing. 10 Crankshaft. 11 Thrust washer, upper. 12 Centre main half bearing. 13 Rear main half bearing. 14 Rear main bearing cap and dowels. 15 Oil sump joint washer, right. 16 Thrust washer, lower. 17 Centre main bearing cap and dowels. 18 Front main bearing cap and dowels. 19 Clamping screw and washer for (20). 20 Connecting rod, less cap. 21 Gudgeon pin. 22 Vee-belt for fan and pulley. 23 Crankshaft pulley. 24 Lockwasher. 25 Starting nut. 26 Connecting rod half bearing. 27 Connecting rod cap. 28 Lockwasher. 29 Setscrew for connecting rod. 30 Oil sump. 31 Cork sealing washer. 32 Set screw and captive washer. 33 Oil sump joint washer, left. 34 Main bearing cap lockwasher. 35 Setscrew for main bearing cap. 36 Setscrew and shakeproof washer for strainer bracket. 37 Oil strainer. 38 Suction pipe. 39 Drain pipe for rear main bearing cap.

section the locating plate must be replaced with a new one. The plate also has a small lubricating hole drilled in it. This must be replaced with the small hole towards the right-hand side of the block.

Check the camshaft bearing journals for wear and scoring, the diameters and clearances being given in the Technical Data section. Examine the bearing liner, or liners, in the cylinder block for signs of scoring or pitting. All the 1098 cc engines, and the 948 cc engines fitted to 'Sprites' I and II, and 'Midget' I, have three steel liners with white-metal bearing surfaces. All the other engines have only one which is at the front, the other two camshaft journals running direct in the block. It is a highly-skilled job to replace these liners and reamer them in position. The camshaft must also be examined for wear of the cams and the distributor drive gear to see if this is enough to warrant renewal.

When the camshaft is being replaced in the block, remember to align the drive pin in the rear end of the cam-shaft with the slot in the end of the oil pump driving spindle so that they will engage properly.

The sump

This is secured to the cylinder block by fourteen bolts, shakeproof washers and flat plates. It can be removed either in or out of the car. With the sump drained and removed it will be possible to see the gauze strainer from which a suction pipe runs up to the oil pump. This can be seen in **FIG 1:6**. Detach this oil pipe from the crankcase and then unscrew the two bracket bolts from the rear main bearing caps, and the strainer will come away. Never use rag to clean the gauze but scrub it well with a stiff brush in petrol and leave to dry. The sump must also be cleaned in the same way. If leaking or damaged, the joint washers should be renewed, every trace of the old washers and any jointing compound being scraped from the joint faces. Now examine the cork sealing washers to be found in half-circular housings at each end of the sump. These seal on

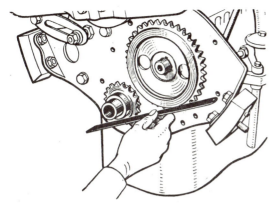

Fig 1:7 Lining up crankshaft and camshaft gear teeth

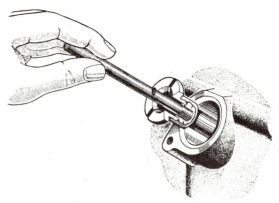

Fig 1:8 Using threaded rod to remove the distributor spindle

the front and rear main bearing caps and the ends should just stand proud of the sump face. If they leak or are damaged they must be renewed. Grease the new packings and press them fully home in the housings, using a round object the same diameter as the crankshaft main journals. The ends should stand proud of the sump by approximately $\frac{3}{32}$ in. The four ends of the joint washers will overlap these raised portions, so that when the sump is replaced the cork is compressed and a perfect oil seal made.

Removing the clutch and flywheel

With the gearbox parted from the engine, the clutch and flywheel can be taken off. Slacken the screws holding the clutch cover flange to the flywheel, doing this a turn at a time and crossing from side to side until the spring pressure is relieved. If the clutch is to be dismantled refer to the appropriate chapter. The four bolts holding the flywheel to the crankshaft are locked by tabs on two locking plates.

With the bolts removed the flywheel and starter ring will pull off the crankshaft register without trouble. The ring is a shrink fit on the flywheel and can be replaced with a new one if worn. Cut partly through the ring with a hacksaw and then split the cut open with a cold chisel, taking care not to damage the register on which the starter ring fits. Now heat the new ring all round to an even light blue surface colour, the equivalent to a temperature of 300°–400°C (575°–752°F). Do not overheat or the hardness of the teeth will be impaired. The heated ring is placed on the flywheel with the cut-away on the gear teeth facing the flywheel register, when it can be tapped lightly into place. Allowed to cool naturally, the ring will be a permanent shrink fit and immovable.

The connecting-rods

The big-ends are fitted with renewable steel-backed bearing shells and are split diagonally. The caps have machined lugs mating with the rods to ensure accurate alignment, the bolts being locked by a plate. The small-ends are split and clamped on the gudgeon pin in the 800 cc and 948 cc engines, see **FIG 1:9**. The 1098 cc engines have rods with bushed small-ends for the fully-floating gudgeon pins shown in **FIG 1:10**. There is a jet on the right-hand side of each rod which lubricates the cylinder wall, the bearing shells being drilled to pass the oil from the big-end supply.

Before splitting the big-ends make certain that each rod and cap is marked with the number of the bore to which it belongs, starting with number 1 at the front. Unlock the bolts and unscrew them about a quarter of an inch. Now tap the bolt heads lightly, when the cap will separate from the rod. Remove any carbon from the top of the cylinder bores and push the pistons and rods upwards and out. The caps and their bolts should now be replaced on the rods in the correct order and the right way round. The bearing shells are steel-backed, the bearing surfaces being in different alloys to suit the power output of the engine. Reference should be made to the Technical Data section at the back of this book for details of the correct type to use. Never mix different bearing alloys in one engine. The bearing surfaces are precision machined and do not require bedding in. Note also that there is a tab on each shell which mates with a notch in the rod or cap. If the shells are scored, pitted or breaking up they must be renewed. All new shells are drilled for the oil jet previously mentioned, so that they may be fitted either to the rod or the cap.

IMPORTANT

Never file the rods, caps or bearing shells, as they at once become non-standard and can never be used to obtain new rods on an exchange basis. On the 1098 cc engines, particular note must be made of the following. Should the piston or connecting-rod suffer damage or the small-end bush need renewing, the pistons and connecting-rods are supplied as matched sets only. In no circumstances should the small-end bush, piston or connecting-rod be renewed separately.

Pistons

The 800 cc and 948 cc engines have split-skirt aluminium alloy pistons with the split adjacent to the clamping bolt in the small-end. An exception is the 948 cc engine in 'Sprite' II and 'Midget' I which is fitted with solid-skirt pistons, but still has the clamped gudgeon pin. To remove the pistons from the connecting-rods, unscrew the clamping bolt from the small-end of the connecting-rod, taking it out completely, and then the gudgeon pin can be pushed free. The piston has four rings, three at the top for compression sealing and the one at the bottom for oil-control. The top one is plain. The next two are taper, and should be fitted with the narrow side uppermost. They

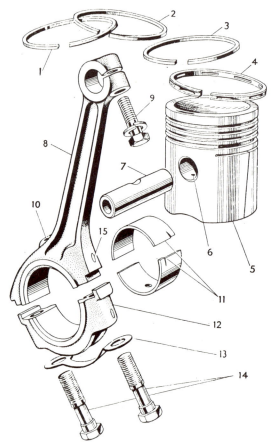

Fig 1:9 Connecting rod and piston assembly for 800 cc and 948 cc engines

Key to Fig 1:9 1 Piston ring, parallel.   2 Piston ring, taper.
3 Piston ring, taper.   4 Piston ring, scraper.   5 Piston.
6 Gudgeon pin lubricating hole.   7 Gudgeon pin.   8 Connecting rod, less cap.   9 Clamping screw and washer.   10 Cylinder
wall lubricating jet.   11 Connecting rod bearings.   12 Connecting rod cap.   13 Lockwasher.   14 Setscrews.
15 Mark on rod and cap.

may also be found to be marked with a 'T'. Oil control-
rings can be fitted either way up. Piston rings must always
be removed upwards over the top of the piston. Use a
narrow piece of thin steel inserted under one end of the
ring and rotate it gently, applying slight upward pressure
on the ring so that it begins to rest on the land above the
ring groove, until the whole ring is out of the groove. All
rings must be replaced from above after cleaning carbon
from the grooves with a piece of broken ring. When in
place in the bore the ring gap between the ends should be
seven- to twelve-thousandths of an inch. This can be
measured by pushing the ring well down the bore, using
a piston to do so.

When the engines are produced, the pistons are fitted
by selective assembly because of very small variations in
size. The grade number is stamped on the piston crown
inside a diamond mark, and this must always coincide
with a similar grading number stamped on the cylinder

block face adjacent to the bore. The piston crown is also
stamped 'FRONT' to show which way round it should be
fitted, and oversize pistons have their size stamped in a
small ellipse. This size must always be stamped on the
cylinder block adjacent to the bore after every rebore.

If the piston clearances given in Technical Data are
exceeded a rebore is necessary. Oversize pistons for the
800 cc and 948 cc engines are available in +.010 in,
+.020 in, +.030 in and +.040 in sizes, and suitable bore
sizes for these are given in Technical Data.

The 1098 cc engine has oversize pistons which are only
available in two sizes, namely +.010 in and +.020 in,
complete with connecting-rods. The 1098 cc pistons are
detached from the connecting-rods by removing both
spring circlips from inside the piston bosses and pushing
out the gudgeon pin. To reassemble, the gudgeon pins
should be a hand push fit at a room temperature of 20°C
(68°F). Replace the circlips, ensuring that they are right
home in their grooves.

The clamped type of gudgeon pin should also be a hand
push fit. To reassemble, line up the groove at the centre of
the pin so that the clamp bolt can be inserted. The bolt
must screw up freely and properly compress the spring
washer. It will not do this if it is bent, in which case it must

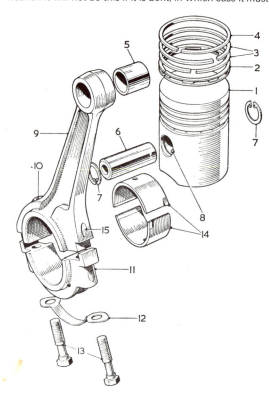

Fig 1:10 Connecting rod and piston assembly for 1098 cc engines

Key to Fig 1:10 1 Piston.   2 Piston ring, scraper.   3 Piston
rings, taper.   4 Piston ring, parallel.   5 Small-end bush.
6 Gudgeon pin.   7 Circlip.   8 Gudgeon pin lubricating hole.
9 Connecting rod.   10 Cylinder wall lubricating jet.   11 Connecting rod cap.   12 Lock washer.   13 Bolts.   14 Connecting rod bearings.   15 Connecting rod and cap marking.

be renewed. Check the fit of the gudgeon pin by holding the piston and connecting-rod assembly horizontally, when the weight of the big-end should be just insufficient to turn the pin in the piston. Oversize gudgeon pins are not available.

If it is necessary to fit cylinder bore liners this can only be done by experts with precision machinery. After the liners are fitted they are finished to the standard bore size.

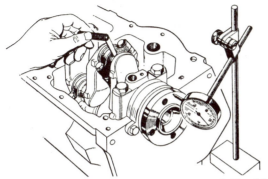

Fig 1:11 Gauging side clearance of connecting rods. The dial indicator is measuring crankshaft end float

Removing the crankshaft and main bearings

The forged steel balanced crankshaft is supported in the crankcase by three main bearings which have renewable shells. These shells are of the steel-backed type which do not need bedding in. The bearing surfaces are of special alloys ranging from white-metal to copper-lead or lead-indium according to the duties of the engine, and reference should be made to the Technical Data before renewing them. Do not mix different alloys in one engine.

On each side of the centre main bearing are thrust washers to control end float of the crankshaft. Before removing the bearing caps, check this end float to see whether the thrust washers need renewal, as shown in **FIG 1:11**. The bearing assembly is clearly shown in **FIG 1:12**. Now mark each bearing cap and the crankcase so that there can be no doubt about the exact location when the cap is replaced. With the rear engine mounting plate removed and the two bolts through the front mounting plate into the side of the front main bearing cap unscrewed, it will be possible to take off each cap. Note the locking plates and the tubular dowels which are shown in **FIG 1:12**. The bottom halves of the thrust washers have tags on them and will come away with the centre cap. Keep the shells with their respective caps. The crankshaft can now be lifted out, the top halves of the bearing shells put with their caps in the right order, and the top halves of the thrust washers removed.

Inspect the crankshaft journals and big-end pins for scoring and ovality, comparing the sizes with those given in Technical Data. If necessary the crankshaft may be reground, but not below −.040 in. Bearing shells are available for the undersizes, −.010 in, −.020 in, −.030 in and −.040 in. Clean the crankshaft oil-ways thoroughly, particularly if any of the bearings have 'run'. Do this by forcing petrol or paraffin through the holes under pressure, following up with clean engine oil. Examine the bearing shells and renew them if they show signs of scoring or breaking away.

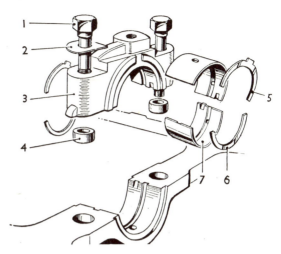

Fig 1:12 Inverted view of centre main bearing. Note tab on lower thrust washer 5

Key to Fig 1:12 1 Main bearing bolts.   2 Lockwasher
3 Main bearing cap.   4 Dowels.   5 Thrust washer, lower
6 Thrust washer, upper.   7 Main bearing shell.

IMPORTANT

Never file the caps to take up wear or reduce running clearances.

When the crankshaft is replaced the thrust washers should have their oil grooves facing outwards.

Like the big-end bearing shells, the main bearing shells will be found to have tabs which fit into notches machined in the caps and the crankcase housings.

The oil pump

Now that the rear engine mounting plate has been removed, the oil pump can be seen at the end of the camshaft tunnel as shown in **FIG 1:5**. Bend back the locking tabs from the three outer bolts and unscrew them so that the pump can be withdrawn. If the pump is withdrawn with the camshaft in place, note the position of the slot in the driving shaft so that it can be lined up with its pin in the camshaft on replacement. **FIG 1:13** shows the Hobourn Eaton pump dismantled to reveal the inner and outer rotors. Replace any worn parts, dropping the outer rotor into the body with the chamfer downwards. There is a later type of Hobourn Eaton pump which has a cover located by two dowels and a machine screw into the front face. The Burman pump shown in **FIG 1:14** is of the sliding vane type. To remove the vanes from the spindle prise off the sleeve at the back end, next to the rear cover. If new parts are fitted, try the spindle of either pump to see that it revolves freely. It is also important to check on the condition of the gasket between the pump face and the cylinder block. It must be in perfect condition and fitted so that the inlet and outlet ports are not restricted.

Oil pressure relief valve

This will be found on the right-hand side of the cylinder block behind the distributor, as in **FIG 1:15**. This valve provides an extra return passage back to the sump if oil pressure becomes excessive when the oil is cold. As the valve lifting pressure is not adjustable it is important to check the free length of the spring and replace it if it is less than $2\frac{7}{8}$ in. Another factor which will affect the relief pressure is the position of the screwed plug, so that it is important to fit the two fibre washers, as shown in the illustration. Examine the seating of the valve cup for wear. If not excessive, it can be ground in using a very little fine compound, every trace of which must be removed after the operation. The relief pressure should be 60 lb/in.^{2}

External oil filters

These are of two types, the early by-pass as shown in **FIG 1:16** and the full-flow shown in **FIG 1:17**. The by-pass filter is thrown away when clogged, but the full-flow filter has a replaceable element. If these filters need attention with the engine in the car, stop the engine before un-screwing anything. To take off the by-pass filter, remove the bracket set screw, then slacken the clip screw and slide off. Unscrew the filter anti-clockwise by hand. When re-placing, make certain that the rubber sealing washer is sound, tighten up by hand and replace the clip and bracket securely.

To inspect the element in the full-flow filter, unscrew the centre bolt from below and take away the casing com-plete with element and oil by keeping the bolt head pressed upwards. Make no attempt to wash the element if it is clogged as dirt may well be forced deeper into the felt. Clean the inside of the casing, put in a new element, fill with oil and replace, keeping the bolt firmly in place or the oil will be lost. If leakage has been evident, replace the sealing washer in the groove under the head, and the washer on the centre bolt. Tighten the bolt sufficiently to make an oil-tight joint, run the engine for a few minutes and top up the sump if necessary.

Reassembling the engine

To start with, it is advisable to provide a complete set of new gaskets. Clean every joint face free from old gasket material and jointing compound. Pay particular attention to such crevices as those behind the crankcase webs where swarf from reboring operations can lodge. Clean out all oil holes with a powerful jet of fluid, following up with some clean engine oil. If the auxiliaries such as the water pump, distributor and mechanical fuel pump have been over-hauled according to the instructions in later chapters, or are in good condition, the work of reassembling the engine can proceed.

Stand the block on its top face and fit the top halves of

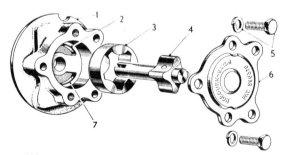

Fig 1:13   The Hobourn Eaton oil pump

Key to Fig 1:13   1 Pump body.   2 Delivery port.   3 Outer rotor.   4 Inner rotor and driving shaft.   5 Setscrew and washer.   6 Cover.   7 Suction port.

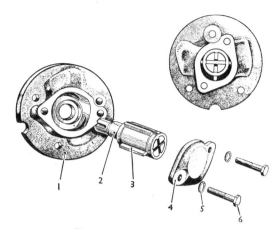

Fig 1:14   The Burman oil pump

Key to Fig 1:14   1 Oil pump flange.   2 Rotor.   3 Vane. 4 Pump cover.   5 Cover bolt washer.   6 Cover bolt.

the main bearing shells into the crankcase housings, in their correct order and with the locating tabs properly inserted in their notches. The top halves of the thrust washers are also fitted. These have no locating tab. Oil liberally and drop the crankshaft carefully into place. With the bottom bearing shells in their correct caps, these can be replaced and the fixing bolts inserted with a locking plate under each.

Tighten the bolts to the torque figure given in Tech-nical Data, starting with the centre bearing. As each cap is tightened check to see that the crankshaft will turn freely. If it does not, remove the last cap to be tightened and look for burrs or dirt under the shell. When it comes to fitting the rear cap, coat the horizontal surfaces with jointing compound. If there has been trouble with oil leakage into the clutch housing look at the rear end of the crankcase where there is the upper half of the housing which collects oil thrown off by the thrower ring on the crankshaft behind the rear bearing. It can be seen in **FIG 1:5** just in front of the rear mounting plate. The half-circular part must be close to, but must not actually touch, the oil-return scroll cut in the crankshaft behind the knife-edged thrower ring. Before fitting the rear cap, verify that this rear cover is exactly flush with the bottom face of the block and has an even clearance all round the top half of the crankshaft. If this is not so, slacken the three fixing set screws, tap the cover into the correct position and re-tighten the screws. The jointing compound on the hori-zontal face of the rear bearing cap will now make a good seal on this rear cover. Lastly, fix the two bolts which go through the front mounting plate into the side of the front bearing cap. There is a locking plate for these two bolts.

Replacing the camshaft, the oil pump, the flywheel and the clutch

Oil the camshaft and slide it into the crankcase. Refit the camshaft locating plate to the front mounting plate with the small oil jet hole facing the right-hand side of the engine. Replace the oil pump, using a new gasket, lining up the slot in the driving spindle with the cross-pin in the end of the camshaft before pressing home. Lock the fixing bolts and then bolt the rear engine mounting plate into position, taking special care of the joint washer so that oil leaks at this point are not possible. The flywheel can now be bolted to the crankshaft, the flange being clean and free from burrs. Lock the four bolts after they have been tightened to the specified torque figure.

When the clutch is bolted to the flywheel, the centre plate must be centralised using the special arbor which is described in the Clutch chapter. Tighten the fixing bolts in the cover flange a little at a time, crossing from side to side.

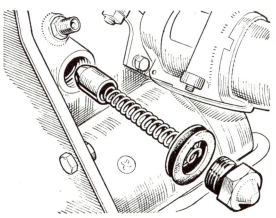

Fig 1:15 Location of the oil pressure relief valve. Note the two fibre washers

Replacing the timing gear

Put the packing washers on the crankshaft behind the small chain wheel. Assemble the two wheels inside the chain with the timing marks in the position shown in **FIG 1:18**. Turn the crankshaft until the key is at tdc and put the camshaft key at one o'clock. Take the wheels and chain together and put the small wheel on the crankshaft until the key engages. Turn the camshaft until its key lines up with the keyway in the large wheel and press both wheels home. Check the timing marks and then secure the camshaft wheel with the lock washer and nut. The next step is to put the dished oil-thrower on the crankshaft with the concave side facing forward as shown in **FIG 1:5**. The timing cover is best replaced with the pulley in place in the seal. Fitting a new seal has been covered in an earlier section. The pulley boss is oiled and inserted into the seal and then the cover and pulley are offered up to the crankshaft. Line up the pulley keyway with the key and press into place. Screw in the cover fixing screws, tightening them gradually and evenly. The pulley securing screw is locked by a plate which engages the pulley keyway. With the screw firmly tightened, a tab can be turned up to lock it.

Fitting the pistons and connecting-rods

Assuming that the rings have been fitted to the pistons and the pistons to their correct connecting-rods according to earlier instructions, they can now be replaced in their original bores, unless they are new. Oil the bores first and use a spring compressor. The ring gaps should be at 90 degs to each other and see that the word 'FRONT' on the piston crown is correctly placed. On split-skirt pistons this can be checked by observing that the split is on the cam-

shaft side of the engine, where the gudgeon pin clamping bolt should be too. Pull the connecting-rod down the bore until the top bearing shell can be pressed into place. Oil the big-end pin and fit the bottom shell into the cap. With the identifying numbers or marks aligned, the cap can be fitted and the bolts inserted with their locking plate under the heads. Tighten to the torque figure required and check that the crankshaft is free to turn. Then lock the bolt heads.

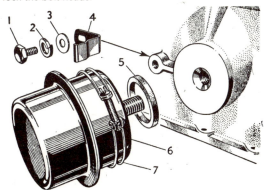

Fig 1:16 The by-pass oil filter withdrawn, showing the clip and bracket assembly

Key to Fig 1:16 1 Setscrews.   2 Spring washer.   3 Plain washer.   4 Oil filter bracket.   5 Rubber seal.   6 Oil filter. 7 Locking clip.

Replacing the sump

Fit the strainer, entering the suction pipe into the tapped hole in the crankcase and then securing the bracket feet to the two rear bearing caps. Tighten the suction pipe nut. Fit new gaskets to the sump if the old ones are at all doubtful, smearing the joint faces with grease. Lift the sump into place, insert the fourteen set screws and tighten them evenly. Each screw should have a shakeproof washer and a plain one.

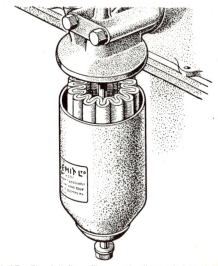

Fig 1:17 The full-flow filter partly dismantled to show the element

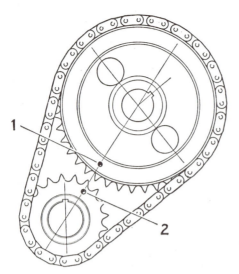

Fig 1:18 The timing gears ready to assemble, with marks 1 and 2 adjacent

Putting on the head

The block must now be standing the right way up so that the tappets can be inserted, oiling each one and replacing it where it came from. The head gasket is fitted dry, the words 'TOP' and 'FRONT' being stamped on it so that there can only be one way for it to go. See that the water by-pass hose at the front end on the left-hand side is in place with the clips fitted but loose. The head can now be lowered squarely into place. Drop the push-rods into their correct holes, making sure that the lower ends enter the tappets properly. The rocker gear is then dropped over the head studs, each push-rod being carefully located under the correct adjusting screw. All the head and rocker pedestal nuts and washers are now screwed on, with the rocker shaft locking plate in position. There are four plates on later engines, one on top of each pedestal. Proceed to tighten the nuts a turn at a time in the sequence given in **FIG 1:19** where it will be seen that the rocker pedestal nuts are tightened as pairs. The torque figures are given in Technical Data. Turn the crankshaft to see that all is well and then adjust the valve clearance.

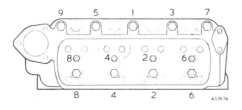

Fig 1:19 The order of loosening and tightening the cylinder head nuts

Valve rocker adjustment

These engines have been designed to run with a valve rocker clearance of .012 in when cold and if good performance is to be maintained the correct clearance is essential. **FIG 1:20** shows a rocker with a feeler gauge between the rocker arm and the valve stem. To adjust the clearance it is necessary to ensure that the valve is closed, with the tappet on the back of the cam opposite to the peak. This can be done by observing the following sequence:

Adjust No. 1 rocker with No. 8 valve fully open.
Adjust No. 3 rocker with No. 6 valve fully open.
Adjust No. 5 rocker with No. 4 valve fully open.
Adjust No. 2 rocker with No. 7 valve fully open.
Adjust No. 8 rocker with No. 1 valve fully open.
Adjust No. 6 rocker with No. 3 valve fully open.
Adjust No. 4 rocker with No. 5 valve fully open.
Adjust No. 7 rocker with No. 2 valve fully open.

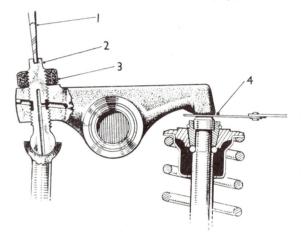

Fig 1:20 Adjusting the clearance between rocker end and valve stem

Key to Fig 1:20 1 Screwdriver. 2 Adjusting screw.
3 Locknut. 4 Feeler gauge.

Notice that the numbers in each line add up to nine. Remembering this, it is easy to go on checking without constant reference to the table. Slacken the locknut just enough to allow the adjusting screw to be turned with a screwdriver until the feeler gauge is very slightly nipped. Then tighten the locknut, keeping the adjusting screw from turning. Always check the clearance after this in case the adjustment has been disturbed in the locking process. A point of great importance is that this clearance adjustment cannot be accurate if the rocker end is pitted through wear.

Oil leakage from the cover can only be prevented by the use of a good gasket correctly positioned. A glance at **FIG 1:2** will show the order for replacing the rubber bush and cup washer on the cover studs. The thermostat is now replaced at the front end of the head, assuming that it is in good condition or has been checked according to the notes in the Cooling chapter. The narrow ring gasket is dropped into the recess in the head, followed by the thermostat and then the triangular joint washer and lastly the elbow, facing to the right. Screw up the by-pass hose clips to finish the head assembly.

Replacing the distributor and drive

Using a long $\frac{5}{16}$ in UNF bolt in the tapped end of the distributor drive shaft, insert it into the right-hand side of the cylinder block after reading the instructions for this operation in the Ignition chapter. The greatest care is essential here, or the ignition timing will be out. With the shaft gear correctly meshed, remove the bolt. Fit the distributor housing using the special bolt and washer provided. These are used because the bolt head must not protrude above the face of the housing. Refit the distributor to the housing, and if the clamp has been disturbed, refer to the Ignition chapter for details of how to re-set the timing.

The fuel pump

Replace the mechanical fuel pump, if one is fitted. Use a good joint washer and feed the rocker arm in carefully so that it is correctly positioned against the eccentric on the camshaft.

Valve timing

Should it be necessary to check the valve timing, look up the figures given in Technical Data for the engine concerned. It is not possible to check the timing accurately unless the normal valve clearance of .012 in is increased to the figure shown with the engine cold. In **FIG 1:21** it can be seen that there is a groove in the rear flange of the crankshaft pulley and a set of three pointers on the timing cover. Turn the crankshaft until the second valve from the front is about to open. This is No. 1 cylinder inlet valve. The groove in the pulley should now be opposite the longest pointer. Although this pointer normally indicates tdc, the increased valve clearance means that the valve will actually open at five degrees before top dead centre. It is most important to restore the valve clearance to the correct setting of .012 in cold.

Replacing the rocker cover and thermostat

With the breather pipe to the front, the rocker cover can now be fitted.

Manifold replacement

If the inlet and exhaust manifolds have been parted,

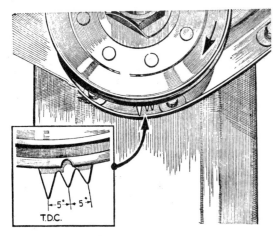

Fig 1:21 The ignition timing pointers. The inset also shows the pulley notch

details of their reassembly were given earlier in the chapter. Note that the four set screws are left finger-tight until the manifolds are installed on the head studs and the stud nuts tightened. Always use a new gasket.

The water pump and generator

These are serviced by referring to the chapters on Cooling and Electrical Equipment, and if satisfactory they can be replaced. Use a new paper joint washer between the pump body and the cylinder block. Refit the generator, leaving the pivot and link bolts finger tight until the belt is put on the pulleys. With the belt in place lift the generator, using a gentle hand pull only. Tighten the three bolts and check the belt. This must not be excessively tight nor so loose that the belt slips. It should be possible to move it laterally about an inch in the middle of the longest run.

The engine assembly is now complete with the exception of the carburetter and air cleaner, which are best fitted after the engine has been replaced in the car. Refill with oil and water. Do not fit the air cleaner until the engine has been run up to working temperature and the rocker clearance checked. After 100 miles tighten the cylinder head nuts to the correct torque reading and give the rocker clearance a final check.

FAULT DIAGNOSIS

Possible fault if engine will not start. Section (a)

1 Defective coil
2 Faulty condenser
3 Dirty, pitted or incorrectly set contact breaker points
4 Ignition wires loose or insulation faulty
5 Water on sparking plug leads
6 Corrosion of battery terminals or discharged condition
7 Faulty or jammed starter
8 Plug leads wrongly connected
9 Vapour lock in fuel pipes
10 Defective fuel pump
11 Over-choking
12 Under-choking
13 Blocked petrol filter or carburetter jets
14 Leaking valves
15 Valve timing incorrect
16 Ignition timing incorrect

If the engine stalls. Section (b)

Check 1, 2, 3, 4, 10, 11, 12, 13, 14 and 15 in Section (a)
1 Plugs defective or gap incorrect
2 Retarded ignition
3 Mixture too weak
4 Water in fuel system
5 Petrol tank breather choked
6 Incorrect valve clearance

If the engine idles badly. Section (c)

Check 1 and 6 in Section (b)
1 Air leak at manifold joints
2 Incorrect slow running adjustment
3 Air leak in carburetter(s)
4 Slow running jet blocked
5 Over-rich mixture
6 Worn piston rings
7 Worn valve stems or guides
8 Weak exhaust valve springs

Engine misfires. Section (d)

Check 1, 2, 3, 4, 5, 8, 10, 13, 14, 15, 16 and 17 in Section (a)

Check 1, 2, 3 and 6 in Section (b)

1 Weak or broken valve springs

Engine overheats. Section (e). See Section (c)

Compression low. Section (f)

Check 14 and 15 in Section (a)

Check 6 and 7 in Section (c)

Check 1 in Section (d)

1 Worn piston ring grooves

2 Scored or worn cylinder bores

Engine lacks power. Section (g)

Check 3, 10, 11, 13, 14, 15 and 16 in Section (a)

Check 1, 2, 3 and 6 in Section (b)

Check 6 and 7 in Section (c)

Check 1 in Section (d)

Check Sections (e) and (f)

1 Leaking joint washers

2 Fouled sparking plugs

3 Automatic advance not functioning

Valves or seats burnt. Section (h)

Check 14 and 15 in Section (a)

Check 6 in Section (b)

Check 1 in Section (d)

Check Section (e)

1 Excessive carbon around valve seat and head

Sticking valves. Section (j)

Check 1 in Section (d)

1 Bent valve stem

2 Scored valve stem or guide

3 Incorrect valve clearance

Excessive cylinder wear. Section (k)

Check 11 in Section (a)

Check Section (e)

1 Lack of oil

2 Dirty oil

3 Dirty air cleaner

4 Piston rings gummed up or broken

5 Badly fitting piston rings

6 Connecting-rods bent

Oil consumption excessive. Section (l)

Check 6 and 7 in Section (c)

Check Section (k)

1 Ring gap too wide

2 Oil return holes in piston choked with carbon

3 Scored cylinders

4 Oil level too high

5 External oil leaks

6 Ineffective valve stem oil seal

Crankshaft and connecting-rod bearing failure. Section (m)

Check 1 in Section (k)

1 Restricted oilways

2 Worn journals or crankpins

3 Loose bearing caps

4 Extremely low oil pressure

5 Bent connecting-rod

Internal water leakage. Section (n). See Section (c)

Poor circulation. Section (o). See Section (c)

Corrosion. Section (p). See Section (c)

High fuel consumption. Section (q). See Section (d)

Engine vibration. Section (r)

1 Loose generator bolts

2 Fan blades out of balance

3 Exhaust pipe mountings too tight

Modifications

These are made from time to time and as the modified parts are not always interchangeable with the originals, the following notes will be helpful.

To improve water sealing a modified cylinder head gasket has been introduced on the 948 cc and 1098 cc engines. This has ferrules round the water holes. The new gasket is interchangeable with the old. To ensure that the valve rocker screw does not work loose, a new rocker assembly has been introduced with the screwed boss increased in depth from $\frac{7}{16}$ in to $\frac{9}{16}$ in. The adjusting screw has also been increased in length from $1\frac{9}{32}$ in to $1\frac{3}{8}$ in. The old and new adjusting screws are interchangeable but the later type of rocker with the thickened boss must only be used in conjunction with the longer screw. The third ring from the piston crown on early engines was plain. A tapered ring is now fitted to improve oil consumption, so that the order is now: (1) plain, (2) taper, (3) taper and (4) oil control. This assembly can be used on early pistons.

Shorter valve guides with a plain bore, and exhaust valves with smaller-diameter stems are fitted to the cylinder heads of later engines. The new valves and guides are interchangeable, in pairs, with the old.

Later engines may be found to have a one-piece inlet and exhaust manifold in which case the instructions dealing with the bolting together of the separate manifolds may be passed over.

CHAPTER 2

CARBURETTERS AND FUEL SYSTEMS

Mechanical fuel pump   Servicing   Electric fuel pump   Servicing   Early Zenith carburetter
Servicing   Later Zenith carburetter   Servicing   SU carburetters   Servicing
Air cleaners   Fault diagnosis

Early cars have mechanical fuel pumps and Zenith carburetters, and later cars have electric fuel pumps and SU carburetters.

The mechanical pump

This is the AC Sphynx 'Y' type, operated by an eccentric on the engine camshaft, and it will be found low down on the left-hand side of the crankcase. Some models have an external priming lever for pumping fuel by hand without running the engine. The pump is shown in section in **FIG 2:1** and an exploded perspective view is seen in **FIG 2:2**. Notice that in a later version of the same pump there is a different arrangement for the valves.

Operation

As the engine camshaft 13 revolves, the eccentric 12 lifts the rocker arm 16 which is pivoted at 17. The arm pulls rod 1 and diaphragm 3 downwards against pressure from the spring 2. Consequent suction in chamber 4 causes fuel to be sucked into the chamber through filter 9 and inlet valve 11. On the return stroke the pressure of spring 2 pushes the diaphragm upwards, forcing fuel through the delivery valve 7 and port 8 into the carburetter. When the carburetter bowl is full and the float needle valve shut, there is no flow of fuel from the pump until more is needed by the engine. This means that the pump chamber remains full, the diaphragm depressed and the

connecting link 15 out of contact with the abutment on rocker arm 16. The arm will then reciprocate idly until a renewed demand for fuel causes the diaphragm to rise. Spring 14 keeps the rocker arm in constant contact with the eccentric to eliminate noise.

Routine servicing

To clean the gauze filter unscrew the cover retaining screw and remove the domed cover. Lift out the filter and clean it with a brush and petrol or with an air jet. Clean out the sediment chamber too. When refitting the cover use a new cork washer if the old one is broken or hard. Also see that there is a good fibre washer under the head of the retaining screw. Do not overtighten.

Dismantling

Referring to **FIG 2:2** do the following, after scratching an alignment mark across the body flanges.
1 Unscrew bolt 1 and remove cover 3.
2 Lift out filter gauze 5 and cork sealing washer 4.
3 Unscrew the five securing screws 23 and separate the pump halves 6 and 21.
4 Unscrew the screws 9 and remove the valve plate 11, the inlet and delivery valves 8, the valve plate gasket 10, the springs 7 and the delivery valve spring retainer 12. See the appended note for reference to the later type of valves.

5 Remove the diaphragm and pull rod assembly by rotating through 90 degs and pulling out. This will release the diaphragm spring 24.

6 Remove the metal washer 20 and the fibre washer 19.

7 Remove the two retaining circlips 16 and washers 13, push out the rocker arm pivot pin 14 which will release the rocker arm 18, the link 15 and the spring 17.

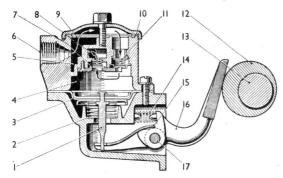

Fig 2:1 Sectional view of AC-Sphynx 'Y' type mechanical fuel pump

Key to Fig 2:1 1 Diaphragm pull-rod. 2 Diaphragm return spring. 3 Diaphragm. 4 Pump chamber. 5 Sediment chamber. 6 Inlet union. 7 Delivery valve. 8 Delivery port. 9 Gauze filter. 10 Cork sealing washer. 11 Inlet valve. 12 Camshaft eccentric. 13 Camshaft. 14 Anti-rattle spring. 15 Connecting link. 16 Rocker arm. 17 Rocker arm pivot pin.

Reassembling

Before proceeding, all the valves should be swilled in clean paraffin as this not only cleans them but helps to improve their sealing.

1 Place the delivery valve 8 on its spring 7 and inlet valve 8 on the deeply recessed seating in the upper casting.

2 Put valve spring 7 on the centre of the inlet valve 8.

3 Position retainer 12 on top of the inlet valve spring 7. The retainer is a small four-legged pressing. Take care not to distort the legs.

4 Lay valve plate gasket 10 in position.

5 Locate valve plate 11 accurately and secure with the three screws 9.

7 With a piece of wire, press downwards on the inlet valve and upwards on the delivery valve to ensure that they work freely.

8 Replace the gauze filter and cover, with new gaskets if necessary.

9 Assemble link 15, packing washers 13, rocker arm 18 and spring 17 in the body 21. Insert rocker arm pin 14 through the hole in the body, at the same time engaging the packing washers 13, the link and the rocker arm. Then spring the clips 16 into the grooves at each end of the pin. The rocker arm pin must be a tap fit in the body. If wear has made it too free, burr the holes in the body slightly.

Fitting the rocker arm can be simplified by pushing a piece of .240 in diameter rod through the hole in one side of the body until it engages the rocker arm washers and the link. The actual pin is then pushed in from the opposite side, removing the guide rod as the pin moves inward.

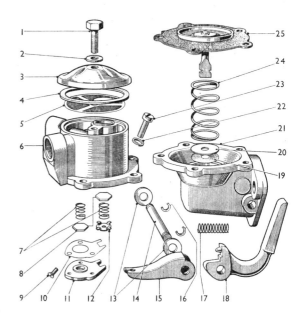

Fig 2:2 Component parts of mechanical fuel pump, type 'Y'

Key to Fig 2:2 1 Cover retaining screw. 2 Fibre washer. 3 Cover. 4 Cork sealing washer. 5 Gauze filter. 6 Upper casting. 7 Valve springs. 8 Inlet and delivery valves. 9 Valve plate screw. 10 Valve plate gasket. 11 Valve plate. 12 Retainer. 13 Packing washers. 14 Rocker arm pivot pin. 15 Connecting link. 16 Retaining clips. 17 Anti-rattle spring. 18 Rocker arm. 19 Fibre washer. 20 Metal washer. 21 Pump body. 22 Spring washer. 23 Upper chamber securing screw. 24 Diaphragm return spring. 25 Diaphragm assembly.

10 Fit the diaphragm assembly to the body by first inserting washer 19, metal washer 20 and spring 24 in the pump body. Place the diaphragm assembly over the spring with the pull-rod downwards, and centre the upper end of the spring in the lower protector washer. The diaphragm should now be put into the position shown in **FIG 2:4**, with the locating tab at twelve o'clock. Press downwards on the diaphragm and turn the assembly anti-clockwise through a quarter of a turn. The slots in the pull rod should now be engaged in the fork in the link. It is possible to push the rod down too far, so check this by measuring the distance from the flange of the pump body to the upper diaphragm protector, with the diaphragm held at the top of its stroke by the spring. This should be approximately $\frac{9}{16}$ in whereas a dimension of $\frac{3}{4}$ in shows that the link is riding on the shoulders of the pull-rod.

11 Fit the two halves of the pump together by pushing the rocker arm until the diaphragm is level with the body flange. Place the upper half of the pump in position by aligning the scratch marks made before dismantling. Replace the five flange screws and lock washers, tightening until the washers are only just engaged. Work the rocker arm several times and finally hold it fully 'up'. The diaphragm will then be right down as in **FIG 2:1** when the screws can be tightened.

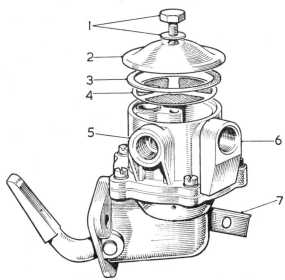

Fig 2:3 Top cover of pump removed to show filter

Key to Fig 2:3 1 Retaining screw. 2 Cover. 3 Cork
sealing washer. 4 Gauze filter. 5 Delivery union. 6 Inlet
union. 7 Priming lever.

Testing

Flush the pump by immersing it in clean paraffin and
work the rocker arm a few times. Empty the pump by
continuing this operation clear of the paraffin. Do not
immerse again, but place a finger over the union socket
marked 'IN' and work the rocker arm several times. When
the finger is removed there should be a distinct sucking
sound. The finger is now placed over the outlet and the
rocker arm pressed inwards. This will have the effect of
compressing air in the pump chamber where the pressure
should be held for two or three seconds. Repeat this
operation with the pump immersed in paraffin and watch
the diaphragm clamping flanges for signs of air bubbles
which denote a leak.

Care is needed when refitting the pump to the engine
to ensure that the rocker arm is correctly positioned against
the eccentric, and not to one side or underneath. Run the
engine and check for leaks at the pipe unions and pump
flanges, after tightening the fixing bolts. Do not forget to
clamp the breather pipe under one of the bolts.

On the later type of pump fitted to 'Sprite' II and
'Midget' I there is a different type of valve. Each valve and
spring is an assembly, both valves being held in place by a
plate. The inlet valve has a spring below the valve and is
replaced in the recess immediately under the large hole to
one side of the sediment chamber. The delivery valve will
have its spring on top. Note that there is a figure-of-eight
gasket between the valves and the body.

The electrically operated fuel pump

There are two types of electric pump in use, the working principles for both being the same. The Austin A40
Mk II uses type SP as in **FIGS 2:5** and **2:6**, and 'Sprite' III
and 'Midget' II use the AUF 200 as in **FIG 2:7**. On all these
cars the pump is located under the floor of the luggage
compartment on the right-hand side.

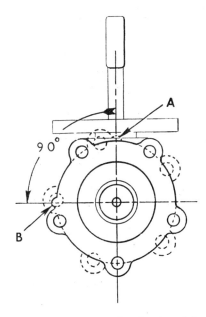

Fig 2:4 Fitting the diaphragm. Turn locating tab from 'A' to
'B' to engage pull rod

Operation

FIG 2:6 shows the pump at rest with diaphragm 10
pressed to the right by spring 12. The armature spindle 29
has pulled the inner rocker 27 to the right so that spring
toggle 17 forces the outer rocker to the left, keeping the
contacts 21 closed. The rockers are mounted on a common hinge pin 28. The outer contact is fixed to spring
blade 22.

The electrical circuit is thus from the terminal screw 24
through the coil winding to the outer spring contact. With
the contacts closed, current then passes by way of the
outer rocker arm and a braided copper wire to the coil
housing back to earth. When the pump is switched on the
solenoid winding 15 is energised, pulling the armature 31
and the diaphragm 10 towards it. The armature assembly
is centralized by a ring of brass rollers 32 which allow
movement to and fro. The partial vacuum to the right of
the diaphragm causes fuel to be drawn into the pumping
chamber of body 8 by way of inlet valve 3. Simultaneously
the armature spindle 29 has moved the inner rocker to
the left, causing the toggle spring 17 to flick the outer
rocker over to the right and so open the contacts. The
break in the electrical circuit de-energises the coil and the
pressure of the feed spring 12 forces the diaphragm to the
right, pushing fuel out through the delivery valve 6. This
movement of the diaphragm and its spindle means that the
inner rocker goes back to the right, the outer rocker to the
left, the contacts are closed and the cycle repeated.

Routine maintenance

Unscrew the inlet nozzle and clean the gauze filter to be
found inside. The contact breaker points can be cleaned
by drawing a strip of paper between them while holding
them lightly together. Make sure that the electrical connections remain tight.

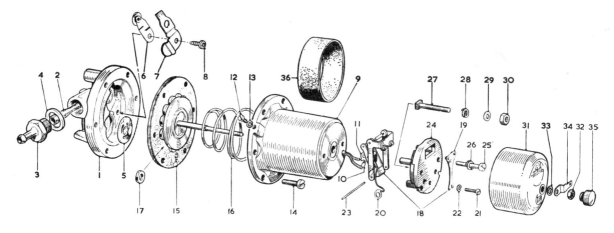

Fig 2 : 5 Later-type SU electric fuel pump exploded

1 Body. 2 Filter. 3 Nozzle inlet. 4 Washer for nozzle. 5 Valve—outlet. 6 Valve—inlet. 7 Retainer—valve.
8 Screw for retainer. 9 Housing—coil. 10 Tag—5 BA terminal. 11 Tag—2 BA terminal. 12 Screw—earth.
13 Washer—spring. 14 Screw—housing to body. 15 Diaphragm assembly. 16 Spring. 17 Roller. 18 Rocker and blade.
19 Blade. 20 Tag—2 BA terminal. 21 Screw for blade. 22 Washer—dished. 23 Spindle for contact breaker.
24 Pedestal. 25 Screw—pedestal to housing. 26 Washer—spring. 27 Screw for terminal. 28 Washer—spring.
29 Washer—lead—for screw. 30 Nut for screw. 31 Cover—end. 32 Nut for cover. 33 Washer—shakeproof.
34 Connector—Lucar. 35 Knob—terminal. 36 Sleeve—rubber.

Dismantling

To avoid confusion between the two models refer to
FIG 2 : 5 for the numbered parts.
1 Unscrew the inlet nozzle 3 and remove, together with
filter and fibre washer.
2 Remove the six coil housing screws 14 and carefully
separate the diaphragm from the two flanges.
3 Unscrew the valve retainer screw 8 and withdraw the
retainer 7 with the two valves 5 and 6.
4 Hold the housing over a bench and unscrew the diaphragm 15 by rotating it anti-clockwise. The eleven
brass rollers 17 will then fall out.
5 Take off the spring 16 and the impact washer (not
shown), but do not attempt to part the spindle from the
diaphragm as this is serviced as a unit.
6 Remove the terminal connections and take off cap 31.
7 Unscrew the spring blade securing screw 21 and remove the long coil lead and the blade. Remove nut 30,
cutting away the lead washer 29 which will be found
flattened underneath it. Unscrew the two pedestal
screws 25 and disconnect the braided copper earth
lead which comes from the outer rocker.
8 Turn the pedestal 24 on its side and remove the remaining coil lead from the terminal screw, then remove the
screw itself.
9 Push out the steel pin 23 and remove the rocker
assembly. Do not remove the toggle springs on the
assembly.
In the case of 'Sprite' III and 'Midget' II, the above
instructions are generally correct, but the following differences should be noted, referring to **FIG 2 : 7** for the part
numbers mentioned.
1 Unscrew the 2BA screws 3 securing the spring clamp
plate 2. This holds the inlet and outlet nozzles 4 in
place. The filter 6 and valve assemblies 7 and 8 can
then be removed, noting the positions of the sealing
washers.

Inspection

Refer to **FIG 2 : 5**.
1 Test each valve assembly in turn by alternately sucking
and blowing at the inlet and outlet connections. The
inlet valve unseats when blowing and seats when sucking; the outlet valve the reverse.
2 Examine the diaphragm for deterioration.
3 If the contact breaker points are badly burned and
pitted, the rocker assembly and spring blade 18 must be
replaced.
4 Check the strength of the feed spring 16. It should
compress to a length of 1 in under a load of $7\frac{1}{2}$ to 8 lb.
In the case of the pump shown in **FIG 2 : 7**, check the
narrow tongues on the valve cages 7 and 8. These retain
the valves and should not be distorted but allow a valve
lift of approximately $\frac{1}{16}$ in.

Assembly of the pump shown in FIG 2 : 5.

1 Replace the valves and inlet connection.
2 Secure the free ends of the rocker assembly to the
pedestal with the pivot pin (see **FIG 2 : 8**). This pin is
hardened and must be replaced by a genuine SU spare
part if it is worn.
3 Fit the square-headed terminal screw to the pedestal.
Replace the spring washer, the short lead from the
coil, a new lead washer and the nut.
4 Slip the braided earth lead from the outer rocker on to
one of the pedestal screws, then a spring washer.
Secure the pedestal with both screws.
5 Fit the remaining coil lead to the 4BA screw and
secure the spring blade to the pedestal with the lead
on top of the blade. The blade must bear against the
small rib as shown by the arrow in **FIG 2 : 11**.
6 Adjust the blade until the points make firm contact
and are a little above the points on the rocker as in
FIG 2 : 9. Move the rocker arm to check that the
points wipe over the centre line of each other.

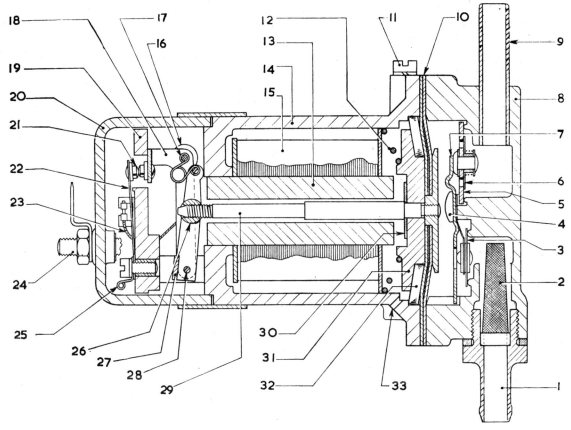

Fig 2:6 Sectional view of SU electric fuel pump

Key to Fig 2:6   1 Feed nozzle.   2 Filter.   3 Inlet valve.   4 Screw—valve retainer.   5 Carrier plate.   6 Delivery valve.
7 Valve retainer.   8 Body.   9 Outlet connection.   10 Diaphragm.   11 Earth screw.   12 Feed spring.   13 Solenoid core.
14 Coil housing.   15 Coil.   16 Fibre rollers.   17 Toggle spring.   18 Outer rocker.   19 Pedestal.   20 End cap.
21 Contact points.   22 Spring blade.   23 Braided earth wire.   24 Terminal screw.   25 Coil lead tag.   26 Trunnion.
27 Inner rocker.   28 Rocker hinge pin.   29 Armature spindle.   30 Impact washer.   31 Armature.   32 Brass rollers.   33 Air vent.

7 With the outer rocker depressed, the spring blade should rest on the rib mentioned previously. If it does not, remove the blade and very lightly set it towards the pedestal. Excessive pressure will restrict the rocker travel.

8 With the impact washer and feed spring in place, pass the armature spindle through the solenoid core and screw it into the trunnion on the inner rocker.

9 Rotate the diaphragm until the outer rocker will just not throw over and then unscrew it seven holes at the diaphragm's edge.

10 Position the brass rollers between the armature and the diaphragm, fit the body to the coil housing and tighten the six screws evenly. It is not necessary to stretch the diaphragm during this operation.

11 Replace the bakelite cap, terminal fittings and the rubber sleeve.

When dealing with the pump fitted to 'Sprite' III and 'Midget' II, as shown in FIG 2:7, there are the following changes in procedure.

After replacing the pedestal on the coil housing, do not fit the contact blade.

2 Fit the diaphragm as in the previous instructions, and with the rollers in place fit and adjust the contacts, removing the contact blade after this. Now hold the coil housing horizontally and push the armature spindle firmly and steadily. Unscrew the diaphragm, pressing and releasing the spindle until the rocker just throws over as in FIG 2:10. Turn the diaphragm back (unscrew it) to the nearest hole and then a further four holes.

3 Replace the inlet and outlet valves in the following order. The valves are identical assemblies. Place the outlet valve assembly, tongue uppermost, in the recess marked 'OUTLET', follow with a joint washer and then the outlet nozzle. With the tongue downwards, place the inlet valve assembly in the deeper recess marked 'INLET', with a joint washer to follow. Now put the filter in the recess with the domed side upwards, then a joint washer and the inlet nozzle. Clamp the nozzles in place so that they will be horizontal when in position in the luggage compartment.

4 Fit and adjust the contact breaker assembly according to the following instructions, which also apply, generally, to the pump fitted to the Austin A40, Mk II.

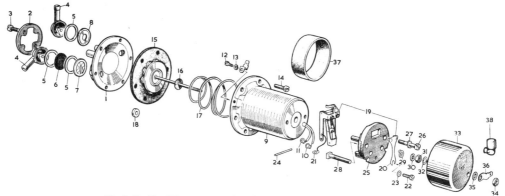

Fig 2:7 The SU pump, type AUF 200, fitted to 'Sprite III' and 'Midget II'

Key to Fig 2:7 1 Body. 2 Spring clamp plate. 3 Screw. 4 Nozzle—inlet/outlet. 5 Sealing washer. 6. Filter. 7 Valve—inlet. 8 Valve—outlet. 9 Housing—coil. 10 Tag—5 BA terminal. 11 Tag—2 BA terminal. 12 Screw—earth. 13 Washer—spring. 14 Screw—housing to body. 15 Diaphragm assembly. 16 Impact washer. 17 Spring. 18 Roller. 19 Rocker and blade. 20 Blade. 21 Tag—2 BA terminal. 22 Screw for blade. 23 Washer—dished. 24 Spindle for contact breaker. 25 Pedestal. 26 Screw—pedestal to housing. 27 Washer—spring. 28 Screw for terminal. 29 Washer—spring. 30 Washer—lead—for screw. 31 Nut for screw. 32 Spacer—nut to cover. 33 Cover—end. 34 Nut for cover. 35 Washer—shakeproof. 36 Connector—Lucar. 37 Packing sleeve. 38 Non-return valve.

5 With the outer rocker back against the coil housing, the contact blade should rest lightly on the small rib on the pedestal face as shown by the arrow in **FIG 2:11**. To adjust, swing the blade sideways, bend slightly and test. Over-tensioning will restrict rocker travel. Hold the blade against the rib without pressing the tip. A .030 in feeler should now pass between the white fibre rollers and the face of the coil housing. Set the tip of the blade to correct this gap.

Later rocker assemblies are to be seen in **FIG 2:12** which shows the gaps which can be checked by feeler gauge. The lift of the contact blade above the pedestal face should be .035 in, bending the stop at the back of the rear contact if necessary. The gap between the rocker finger and the coil housing should be .070 in. The finger can be bent to obtain this gap.

Testing the pump

With the pump fitted and the fuel lines connected, switch on. If the pump is noisy and operates rapidly, an air leak is probable. Check by disconnecting the fuel line from the carburetter and turning the pipe down into a jar. Keeping the end submerged with the pump switched on, the emission of continuous bubbles will confirm an air leak. Check that the inlet union to the pump is tight and that all connections from the tank to the pump are in good order. Check also that the coil housing screws securing the diaphragm flanges are evenly tightened.

If the pump operates without delivering fuel check for a serious air leak on the suction side or foreign matter under the valves, particularly the inlet.

Remove the valves for cleaning

If the pump works initially but the carburetter float

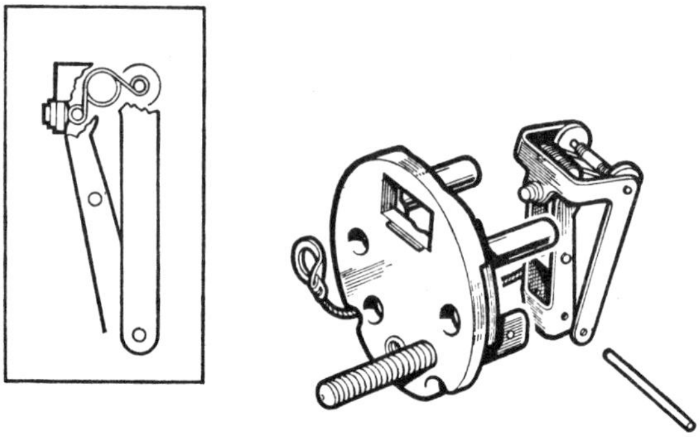

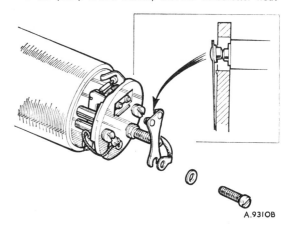

A.9310B

Fig 2:8 Fitting early-type rocker assembly to pedestal. Inset shows correct position of toggle spring

Fig 2:9 Setting the blade and rocker contact points for correct relative position

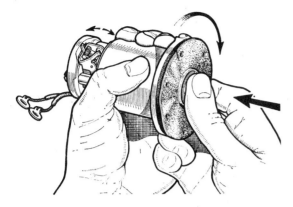

Fig 2:10 Screwing in the diaphragm until the rocker ceases to throw-over

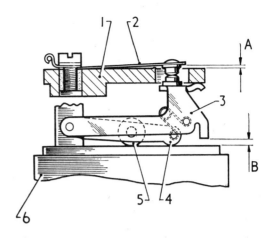

Fig 2:12 The rocker finger settings on later-type assemblies

Key to Fig 2:12 A .035 in±.005 in. B .070 in±.005 in. 1 Pedestal. 2 Contact blade. 3 Outer rocker. 4 Inner rocker. 5 Trunnion. 6 Coil housing.

chamber does not fill, look for an obstructed float needle. Disconnect the fuel line from the carburetter, switch on and check the flow from the open pipe. If it diminishes rapidly and the pump slows down, check the petrol tank venting by removing the filler cap. Blocked or inadequate venting causes a slow power stroke of the pump, burning the contact points.

If the reduced flow is accompanied by slow operation of the pump, check for a clogged filter at the pump inlet. If the pump operates rapidly, check for air leaks, dirt under the valves or faulty valve sealing washers where fitted.

If there is no flow check the electrical supply. If satisfactory, check the contact breaker points. With the main supply lead connected, short across the contacts with a piece of bare wire. If the pump then makes a stroke the fault is due to dirt, corrosion or maladjustment of the contacts.

If the pump will only operate with the inlet pipe disconnected, there may be a restriction in the pipe between the pump and the tank. If compressed air is used to clear a pipeline, never pass it through the pump as the valves will be damaged.

If all these checks fail to locate the trouble, suspect a stiffening of the diaphragm fabric or abnormal friction in the rocker mechanism. Remove the coil housing and flex the diaphragm a few times, taking care not to lose the eleven rollers under it. Assemble the diaphragm as previously instructed and use a little thin oil on the 'throw-over' spring spindles where they pivot in the brass rockers.

Renew the solenoid assembly if there is excessive sparking at the contact points. Do not attempt to cure leakage of the diaphragm joint by applying any kind of jointing compound.

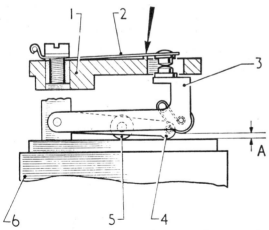

Fig 2:11 The contact gap setting on earlier-type rocker assemblies

Key to Fig 2:11 1 Pedestal. 2 Contact blade. 3 Outer rocker. 4 Inner rocker. 5 Trunnion. 6 Coil housing. A=.030 in.

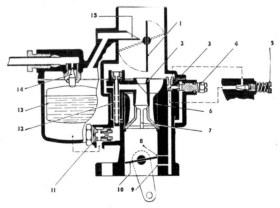

Fig 2:13 A sectional view of the Zenith carburetter, type 26 J.S., fitted to early A30's

Key to Fig 2:13 1 Strangler flap. 2 Inner venturi. 3 Air jet. 4 Slow running jet. 5 Air regulating screw. 6 Choke tube. 7 Deflector. 8 Progression outlet. 9 Slow running outlet. 10 Throttle flap. 11 Main jet. 12 Emulsion tube. 13 Float. 14 Needle. 15 Air release tube.

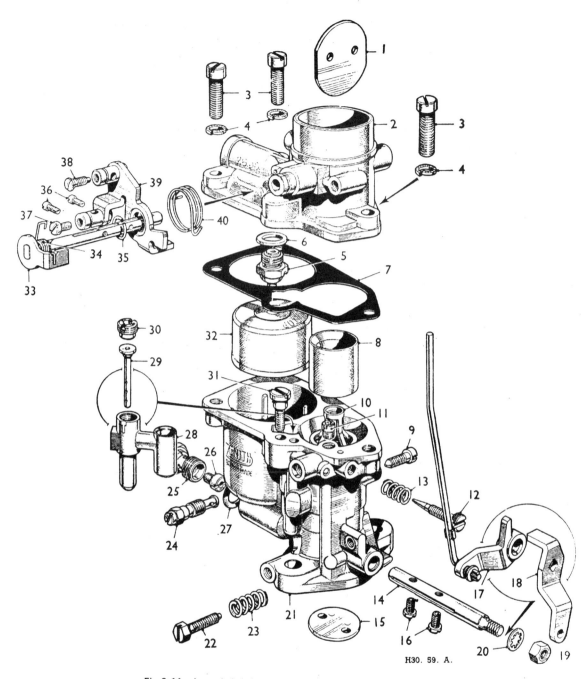

Fig 2:14   An exploded view of the early-type Zenith 26 JS carburetter

Key to Fig 2:14   1 Strangler flap.   2 Strangler body.   3 Strangler body to carburetter screw.   4 Spring washer.
5 Needle seating.   6 Washer.   7 Gasket.   8 Choke tube.   9 Choke tube fixing screw.   10 Deflector.
11 Slow running air bleed jet.   12 Air regulating screw.   13 Spring.   14 Throttle spindle.   15 Throttle.   16 Throttle fixing screws.
17 Floating lever and interconnection rod assembly.   18 Throttle lever.   19 Throttle lever fixing nut.   20 Shakeproof washer.
21 Carburetter body.   22 Throttle stop screw.   23 Throttle stop screw spring.   24 Slow running jet.   25 Main jet carrier.
26 Main jet.   27 Fibre washer for main jet carrier.   28 Inner venturi.   29 Emulsion tube.   30 Main air jet.
31 Inner venturi fixing screw.   32 Float.   33 Strangler spindle.   34 Strangler spring.   35 Strangler lever retaining clip.
36 Strangler flap fixing screws.   37 Interconnection swivel screw.   38 Strangler swivel screw.   39 Strangler lever.
40 Strangler lever spring.

Early A30 carburetter

This down-draught carburetter is the Zenith, type 26 JS. **FIG 2:13** shows it in section, **FIG 2:14** is an exploded view.

Operation

When starting from cold the strangler flap 1 in **FIG 2:13** is closed by the dashboard control. The inter-connecting rod assembly shown in **FIG 2:14** opens the throttle flap slightly at the same time. Rich mixture will now be delivered for starting the engine. Immediately the engine fires a stronger depression will be created on the engine side of the flap, and as this is held closed only by the tension on the spindle spring, the strangler flap will open and close rapidly with pulsations from the engine suction, thus providing a weaker mixture as the engine speeds up.

When the engine is warm enough the strangler can be opened fully. With the throttle closed to the idling position mixture is supplied by the slow-running jet 4 in **FIG 2:13**, to which reference should be made for all the following numbers. Engine suction will be concentrated on outlet 9 and then, by way of drilled passages, to the slow-running jet 4. The output from this jet is controlled by the slow-running screw 5, which acts as an air bleed. The progression outlet 8 provides more fuel as the throttle continues to open until the high depression in the choke tube 6 causes petrol to be drawn from the emulsion tube 12. This petrol joins the intake air to form an emulsion which is drawn into the engine. The emulsion tube is drilled throughout its length. As the petrol level in the tube falls, these holes are uncovered to provide compensation for the main jet 11.

Dismantling the 26 JS

Thoroughly clean the outside of the carburetter, and then refer to **FIG 2:14**.

1 Unscrew the swivel screw 37 enough to allow the strangler body 2 to be drawn off after removing screws 3. Tip out float 32 and store safely.

2 From the strangler body remove the needle seating 5 and washer 6.

3 Remove the strangler flap 1 by unscrewing the two screws 36, so that the spindle 33 can be withdrawn after unhooking spring 34. Mark the flap before removing it as the bevelled edges can only be fitted one way round. Also note the correct position of the strangler spindle and spring with reference to the strangler lever.

4 Clip 35 holds the lever 39 in position. Undo this and slip off the lever and the spring 40.

5 Close the throttle and note the relative positions of the floating lever assembly 17 and throttle lever 18. Note the way the bevelled edges of the throttle fit the bore of the carburetter, and then unscrew the two screws 16 and withdraw the throttle. Pull out the spindle 14 with the floating lever assembly and the throttle lever, leaving the washer 20 and nut 19 in position. Take out the throttle stop screw 22 and spring 23.

6 Remove the main jet carrier 25, and unscrew the main jet 26. With a screwdriver remove the air regulating screw 12, the slow-running jet 24, the slow-running air bleed 11 and the main air jet 30 which holds down the emulsion tube 29.

7 On type 26 JS-2 carburetters the screw 31 can be taken out to allow the venturi 28 to be removed. Screw 9 when detached will permit the removal of choke tube 8 and deflector 10.

8 On type 26 JS-3 carburetters the screw 31 secures the discharge nozzle, and screw 9 a modified choke tube. The inner venturi 28 and the deflector 10 are deleted.

Reassembling the 26 JS

Clean all the parts with petrol, and clear the jets with compressed air if possible. Do not push wire through the jets. Note that all the jet sizes are clearly marked. The higher the number the larger the jet. Refer to Technical Data for correct jet sizes.

Now follow the dismantling procedure in reverse. On type 26 JS-3 carburetters ensure that the bar in the choke tube contacts the beak of the discharge nozzle before the choke tube fixing screw is fitted. Change the gasket 7 between the strangler body and the carburetter body if it is damaged. Replace the float with the word 'TOP' uppermost.

The carburetter on the later A30 and 948 cc A35 cars

This is the Zenith, type 26 VME, illustrated in **FIGS 2:15** and **2:16**.

Operation

The throttle and strangler inter-linkage is similar to that on the type 26 JE carburetter, but there are many changes which will affect the sequence of operations, assuming that the engine has reached working temperature. With the throttle closed to the idling position, mixture will be supplied by the slow-running jet 9 in **FIG 2:15**. Depression will be concentrated on the outlet 2 and from there to the slow-running jet 9 where it is regulated by the slow-running screw 5. Petrol will be drawn from the well 12 beneath the jet. When the throttle is opened slightly, depression is concentrated on the larger outlet 1 to give a progressive getaway from the initial slow-running position. Further opening of the throttle will concentrate the depression upon nozzle 6. Petrol will then be drawn from

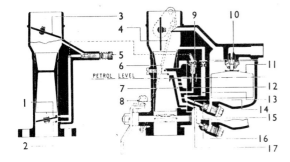

Fig 2:15 A sectional view of the Zenith 26 V.M.E. carburetter

Key to Fig 2:15 1 Progression outlet. 2 Slow running outlet. 3 Strangler flap. 4 Interconnecting rod. 5 Air regulating screw. 6 Emulsion block outlet nozzle. 7 Emulsion tube. 8 Throttle stop screw. 9 Slow running jet. 10 Needle seating. 11 Float. 12 Well (slow running). 13 Well (compensating jet). 14 Compensating jet tube. 15 Compensating jet. 16 Main jet. 17 Main jet tube.

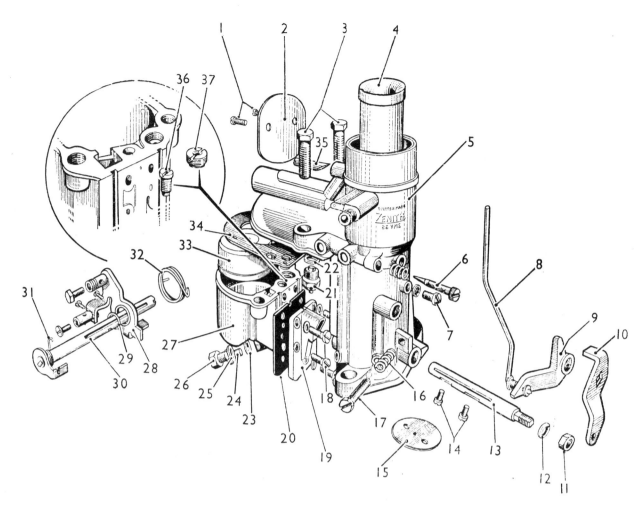

Fig 2:16   An exploded view of the Zenith 26 V.M.E. carburetter.

Key to Fig 2:16   1 Strangler flap fixing screws.   2 Strangler flap.   3 Fixing screws (bowl to barrel).   4 Choke tube.
5 Carburetter body.   6 Air regulating screw.   7 Choke tube fixing screw.   8 Interconnection rod.   9 Floating lever.
10 Throttle lever.   11 Throttle lever fixing nut.   12 Spring washer.   13 Throttle spindle.   14 Throttle fixing screws.
15 Throttle.   16 Throttle stop screw spring.   17 Throttle stop screw.   18 Emulsion block fixing set screws.
19 Emulsion block.   20 Gasket for emulsion block.   21 Needle seating.   22 Washer for needle seating.
23 Compensating jet washer.   24 Compensating jet plug.   25 Main jet washer.   26 Main jet plug.   27 Float chamber.
28 Strangler lever.   29 Retaining clip for strangler lever.   30 Strangler spindle.   31 Strangler spring.
32 Spring for strangler lever.   33 Float.   34 Gasket (bowl to barrel).   35 Air release tube.   36 Slow-running jet.
37 Screw over capacity well.

passages 13 and 7 where there is a reserve of petrol for
instant acceleration. When this is used the supply is from
the main and compensating jets 16 and 15. When the
petrol in well 13 has been consumed the top of the well
is open to atmosphere and the compensating jet 15 becomes an air bleed. Petrol from the main jet 16 meets
emulsified petrol from the compensating jet in a common
channel 7 where it also becomes emulsified. The mixture
is then drawn from the emulsion block nozzle 6. As petrol
is used float 11 will fall, opening the needle valve in seating 10 to allow more petrol to enter the chamber.

Dismantling the 26 VME

The parts can be identified in **FIG 2:16**.
1 Remove the float chamber 27 by unscrewing bolts 3
   and put the float in a safe place.
2 Remove the main and compensating jet plugs 26 and
   24 from underneath the float chamber. A screwdriver
   will take out the jets. The slow-running jet 36 and
   screw 37 may also be unscrewed. Take out the five
   screws 18 and remove the emulsion block 19, taking
   particular care of the joint washer 20.

3 The float needle seating 21 can be removed from the carburetter body 5. Part the strangler flap 2 from the spindle 30 by removing screws 1 and withdraw the spindle after unhooking spring 31. Note the bevels on the flap edges to ensure correct replacement, and also the position of the strangler spring with respect to lever 28.

4 Disconnect the interconnection rod 8 from its upper end. Undo clip 29 which holds the strangler lever in position. Slip off the lever and spring, noting the correct assembled position.

5 Close the throttle and take note of the relative positions of the floating lever and interconnection rod assembly 9 and 8, and the throttle lever 10. Notice that the bevelled edges of the throttle fit closely in the bore of the carburetter body before removing screws 14 and withdrawing the throttle. Take out spindle 13 with the interconnection rod assembly and the throttle lever 10, leaving behind nut 11 and washer 12.

6 Take out throttle stop screw and spring 17 and 16, also air regulating screw 6 with its spring. Detach screw 7 to remove the choke tube 4. Wash all the parts in clean petrol and blow compressed air through all drilled passages. Failing an air supply, a bicycle pump can be used.

Reassembling the 26 VME

This is a straightforward reversal of the dismantling procedure.

Change gasket 34 between the float chamber and the carburetter body if it is damaged. Replace the float with the word 'TOP' uppermost.

Zenith carburetter adjustment (both models)

It will be impossible to obtain the best performance from the carburetter if the air cleaner is clogged, if ignition settings are incorrect, or if there is serious wear in the valve guides and air leaks at other points. These leaks can occur at the carburetter spindles if they are worn, and at any gaskets and joint faces which are damaged. Trouble is often caused by the float feed, which may be due to a worn or sticking needle or a punctured float. The float can be tested by immersing completely in hot water when bubbles will rise from a leak.

If starting is difficult and petrol is reaching the float chamber, check the strangler control and interlinkage. With the strangler flap closed, the throttle should be open a fraction, and this can be adjusted at the top end of the interlinkage rod. Assuming that the engine has started and has reached working temperature, check the idling performance. Heavy 'thumping' slow running with black smoke from the exhaust pipe indicates a rich mixture which can be corrected by turning the regulating screw in an anti-clockwise direction, when the engine speed should increase, with smoother running. The speed can now be reduced to correct idling by means of the throttle stop screw, which is also turned anti-clockwise. Another slight adjustment of the slow-running mixture regulating screw may be needed until the idling is smooth. Very slow idling is not necessary.

Weak mixture can be corrected by turning the regulating screw clockwise. The screw is number 9 in **FIG 2:14** and 6 in **FIG 2:16.**

The air cleaner

On the Zenith carburetters this is an oil-wetted type. To remove it disconnect the breather pipe, slacken the clamp bolt and lift off. Clean the wire mesh element in petrol, allow to dry then re-oil with engine oil. Let this drain before replacing on the carburetter.

SU carburetters, types HS1 and HS2

These carburetters are fitted to the 1098 cc A35, the 948 and 1098 cc A40's and all the 'Sprites' and 'Midgets'. The HS1 fitted to 'Sprite' I has a different jet construction, and the synchronising technique is not the same as that for the later 'Sprites' and 'Midgets', so these points will be covered separately. There are also two types of float mechanism, but apart from this the basic principles of the carburetters are identical.

Operation

Using **FIG 2:17** as a guide, the SU carburetter action can be followed. The body 2 is fitted with the usual butterfly throttle valve 37. On the air intake side of this valve is a variable choke aperture formed by piston 6 rising and falling inside a top chamber 6. This action is automatic, depending as it does upon the depression arising from throttle opening and engine load. The variable volume of intake air needs a varying flow of petrol, which is achieved by using a tapered needle 19 attached to the piston. This rises and falls in a fixed jet aperture 13 giving the greatest flow when the piston is at the top of its travel. Rapid fluctuations of the piston are damped out by an hydraulic damper 8. Rich mixture for starting is obtained by pulling the jet downwards to a smaller diameter of the tapered needle, so increasing the area of the annulus and the flow of petrol. The spring 10 is fitted to assist gravity to return the falling piston.

Removing

If there is only one carburetter, take off the air cleaner, followed by the mixture and throttle controls, the suction pipe which goes to the distributor and the fuel pipe.

In the case of a twin installation, disconnect the breather pipe and remove the centre securing nut and washer from the tie bracket between. Remove the central bolts from the air cleaners and lift them off. Disconnect the mixture and throttle cables, the distributor suction pipe and the fuel pipe. For 'Sprites' II and III and 'Midgets' I and II, release the interconnecting coupling tension springs and the throttle stop return spring. Remove the nuts and spring washers securing the carburetters and lift off. The interconnecting couplings are fitted in sleeved nuts so that the couplings can be slipped out from both carburetters after removal. If the heat shield is removed note that it has a gasket on each face.

For 'Sprite' I, remove the air cleaners as above, the stirrup coupling the jet levers, the throttle return spring, the mixture and throttle control cables. Slacken one of the spring couplings which connect the throttle spindles. Leave this coupling slack on replacement so that the two carburetters can be synchronised. Note the previous remarks about the heat shield gaskets.

Dismantling the HS2

Before stripping anything, mark the relative positions of throttle and control levers. Scratch a line across the flanges

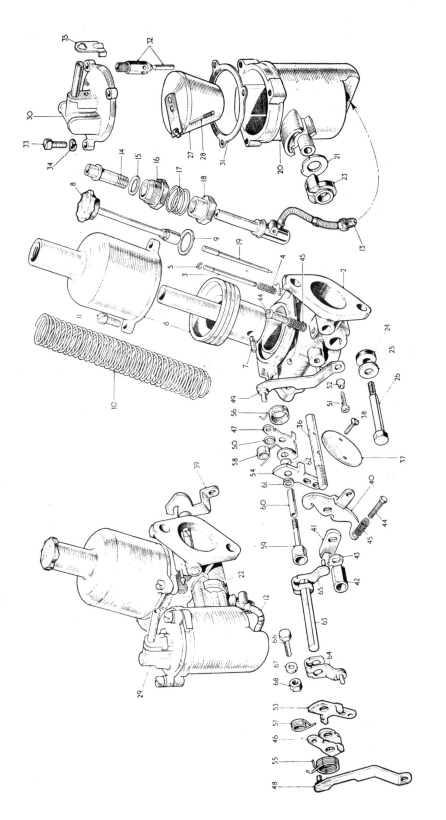

Fig 2:17 Twin SU carburetters, type H.S.2

Key to Fig 2:17 1 Carburetter body (left). 2 Carburetter body (right). 3 Piston lifting pin. 4 Spring. 5 Circlip. 6 Piston chamber assembly. 7 Screw. 8 Cap and damper assembly. 9 Fibre washer. 10 Piston spring. 11 Screw. 12 Jet assembly (left carburetter). 13 Jet assembly (left carburetter). 14 Bearing. 15 Washer. 16 Screw. 17 Spring. 18 Screw. 19 Needle. Float-chamber. 21 Support washer. 22 Rubber grommet (left carburetter). 23 Rubber grommet (right carburetter). 24 Washer (rubber). 25 Washer (steel). 26 Bolt. 27 Float assembly. 28 Lever pin. 29 Float-chamber lid (left carburetter). 30 Float-chamber lid (right carburetter). 31 Washer. 32 Needle and seat assembly. 33 Screw. 34 Spring washer. 35 Baffle plate. 36 Throttle spindle. 37 Throttle disc. 38 Screw. 39 Throttle return lever (left carburetter). 40 Throttle return lever (right carburetter). 41 Lost motion lever. 42 Nut. 43 Tab washer. 44 Throttle screw stop. 45 Spring. 46 Pick-up lever (left carburetter). 47 Pick-up lever (right carburetter). 48 Link (left carburetter). 49 Link (right carburetter). 50 Washer. 51 Screw. 52 Bush. 53 Cam lever (left carburetter). 54 Cam lever (right carburetter). 55 Pick-up lever spring (left carburetter). 56 Pick-up lever spring (right carburetter). 57 Cam lever spring (left carburetter). 58 Cam lever spring (right carburetter). 59 Bolt. 60 Tube. 61 Spring washer. 62 Distance piece. 63 Jet rod. 64 Lever and pin assembly (left carburetter). 65 Lever and pin assembly (right carburetter). 66 Bolt. 67 Washer. 68 Nut.

of the body and piston chamber so that they can be mated accurately on assembly. Refer to **FIG 2:17**.

1 Remove the damper 8 and invert the carburetter to pour off the thin damper oil inside. Remove screws 11 and lift off the piston chamber and piston 6 with spring 10. This is a piece of precision engineering and must be treated with great care.

2 Remove the float chamber cover 30 looking out for the loose float needle 32 if the float hinge pin 28 is taken out. Preserve gasket 31 carefully.

3 Detach the nylon fuel pipe 13 from the float chamber which can then be released by unscrewing bolt 26.

4 The jet 13 can be pulled out, but if the assembly 14 to 18 is disturbed then the jet will need re-centring.

5 Piston lifting pin 3 is held in place by circlips 5. It is used for carburetter tuning.

With the damper still removed, check that the piston is quite free in the piston chamber. Clean carefully if there is any sign of sticking, and oil the piston rod with thin oil. There should be no metallic contact between the piston rim and the inside of the piston chamber. Do not oil any other part but the piston rod. If a needle is to be changed slacken screw 7. Correct needle sizes are given in Technical Data. Insert the new needle so that its shoulder is flush with the bottom face of the piston. Refer to **FIG 2:18** to check the position of the float, as this controls the fuel level in the jet. Insert a piece of round bar between the hinged lever and the lip of the float chamber lid. The end of the lever should just rest on the bar. If it does not, reset by bending at point C. Do not bend the lever, which must be quite flat and at right-angles to the needle when it is on its seating.

The float and lever are different on the 948 cc A40 and on 'Sprite' II and 'Midget' I. **FIG 2:19** shows the method of setting for correct fuel level. Insert a $\frac{5}{16}$ in round bar between the float lever and the lid. The lever fork should just touch the bar when the needle is seated. Set by bending where the fork joins the shank, as the shank must always be flat and at right-angles to the needle.

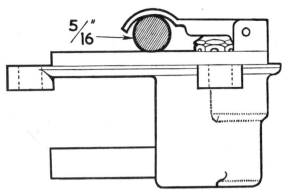

Fig 2:19 Checking the float lever on early SU carburetters

Reassembly

Follow the dismantling process in reverse. Take care to position the keyway in the piston over the key in the body. Before replacing the damper pour in thin oil until it is within $\frac{1}{2}$ in of the top of the piston rod, and check the piston for free movement. It should drop with a smart click. This check can also be done with the carburetter fitted and is necessary if the engine is reluctant to start and will not accelerate. This may be due to a sticking piston, caused by dirt or a badly centred jet.

To centre the jet, referring to FIG 2:20

1 Disconnect the link between the jet lever and the jet head.

2 Remove the nylon tube from the float chamber and withdraw the jet.

3 Remove jet adjusting nut 2 and spring. Replace the jet.

4 Slacken jet locking nut 1 until the jet bearing is just free to rotate.

5 With the damper removed, press the piston down fully and tighten the jet locking nut, keeping the jet in the correct angular position for the nylon tube to be recoupled to the float chamber.

6 The piston should now fall freely with a metallic click. Fully lower the jet and check the sound. If it differs repeat the centring operation, replacing the jet adjusting nut 2 and spring, when successful.

Carburetter adjustment on the HS2

If the tapered needle is stationary the jet aperture can be increased by lowering the jet, and decreased by raising it. This is the basic operation when tuning an SU carburetter. Run the engine up to working temperature and then set the throttle stop screw for fast idling, see **FIG 2:21**. With the jet head firmly in contact with the jet adjusting nut, turn the nut up or down until the engine runs smoothly. Check this by raising the piston about $\frac{1}{32}$ in with a penknife blade or the piston lifting pin 5 in **FIG 2:21**. If the engine stops the mixture is weak. If the speed of the engine continues to increase with the piston raised as much as $\frac{1}{4}$ in the mixture is too rich. If $\frac{1}{32}$ in gives a slight momentary increase in engine speed the mixture is correct. Now set the throttle stop screw for the desired slow running. The fast-idling screw 4 in **FIG 2:21** is adjusted by pulling on the dash panel control knob until the linkage is about to move the jets. This will be about $\frac{1}{4}$ in. Adjust the fast-idling screw to give an engine speed of 1000 rpm when hot.

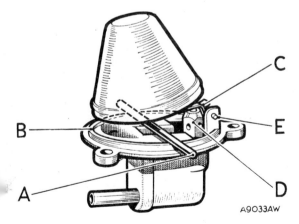

A9033AW

Fig 2:18 Checking the float lever adjustment on later SU carburetters

Key to Fig 2:18   A $\frac{1}{8}$ to $\frac{3}{16}$ in.   B Machined lip.   C Angle of float lever.   D Float needle and seat assembly.   E Lever hinge pin.

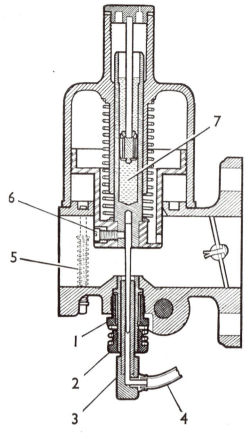

Fig 2:20 A section through the later-type SU carburetter

Key to Fig 2:20 1 Jet locking nut.   2 Jet adjusting nut.
3 Jet head.   4 Nylon fuel pipe.   5 Piston lifting pin.
6 Needle securing screw.   7 Piston damper oil well.

Synchronizing the twin carburetters

On 'Sprites' II and III and 'Midgets' I and II the inter-connection between the throttle spindles must be freed by slackening the pinch bolts 66 shown in **FIG 2:17**. Open each throttle by one turn on the stop screw from the closed position. Remove the piston and chamber assembly and disconnect the choke cable. Using the jet adjusting nuts 2 in **FIG 2:20** set the tops of the jets flush, or as nearly flush as possible, with the bridge inside the intake of the body, until the jet positions are identical. Replace the piston and chamber assembly and check the piston for free fall. Turn down the jet adjusting nuts two turns.

Start the engine and listen at the air intakes with a piece of tubing. Turn the throttle stop screws until the intensity of the hiss at both intakes is the same. The throttles are now synchronized.

Proceed to adjust the mixture strength of each carburetter as instructed under 'Carburetter adjustment'. Firing should be regular and even. If there is irregular misfiring and a colourless exhaust the mixture is weak. A heavy regular misfiring with black smoke from the exhaust indicates a rich mixture.

Twin carburetter throttle linkage

The throttles are operated by a pin and forked lever, see 65 and 41 in **FIG 2:17**. There must be clearance between the pin and fork with the throttle closed. To set this clearance refer to **FIG 2:22**.

With the throttle shaft levers free, put a .012 in feeler between the throttle shaft stop at the top, and the heat shield. Move the throttle shaft lever down until the lever pin rests lightly on the lower arm of the throttle lever fork. Tighten the clamp bolt of the throttle shaft lever. Deal with both carburetters and remove the feeler.

Reconnect the choke cable and set the fast-idling screws as mentioned under 'Carburetter adjustment'.

The HS1 carburetters fitted to 'Sprite' I

An exploded carburetter and control gear is illustrated in **FIG 2:23**. The difference between the HS1 and HS2 carburetters lies mainly in the jet construction and the throttle linkage. Because the jet is surrounded by petrol it is necessary to provide sealing glands at the top and bottom, as can be seen in **FIGS 2:23** and **2:24**. Note the cork rings 24. If there is leakage round the jet these rings must be replaced. It is important to assemble the parts in the order shown, taking care to insert the brass washers 25 with their cupped faces towards the cork rings.

Centring the HS1 jet

Remove the jet and unscrew the adjusting nut. Take off the spring, and replace the nut, screwing it right home. Replace the jet by pushing it in as far as it will go. Unscrew the oil damper and try the piston for freedom. If it does not fall freely with an audible click, slacken the jet sealing nut 16 until the jet bearing 23 is just free. Hold the piston down whilst tightening the jet sealing nut, testing afterwards to hear if the piston is free. Replace the adjusting nut spring when successful. If the SU carburetter is to function properly then correct centring of the jet is absolutely essential.

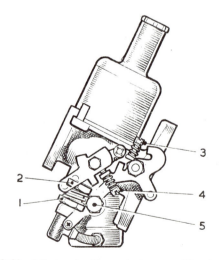

Fig 2:21 Adjustment points on the later-type SU carburetters

Key to Fig 2:21 1 Jet adjusting nut.   2 Jet locknut.
3 Throttle stop screw.   4 'Fast-Idle' adjustment screw.
5 Float-chamber securing bolt.

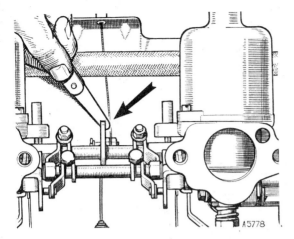

Fig 2:22 Using a feeler gauge between the throttle shaft stop and the heat shield—twin H.S.2's

Carburetter adjustment on 'Sprite' I

1 Remove the breather pipe from the valve cover and take off the air cleaners.
2 Keep the spring coupling between the throttle spindles slackened off and release the jet lever stirrup so that both throttles and jets are independent.
3 Close both throttles by unscrewing the stop screws and then give one turn to the rear screw to get fast idling. The front carburetter remains inoperative, and this can be further ensured by lifting its piston $\frac{1}{2}$ in.
4 Correct the mixture strength of the rear carburetter according to the instructions under 'Carburetter adjustment on the HS2'.
5 When the rear carburetter is adjusted, close its throttle completely and open the front one, lifting the rear piston $\frac{1}{2}$ in. Repeat the jet adjustment operations on the front carburetter.
6 Set the throttles for slow running and synchronization.

Slow running and synchronization on the 'Sprite' I

With the throttle spindles still uncoupled, open each throttle from the fully closed position by making one turn on the stop screws. Now start the engine. Unscrew each stop screw an equal amount until the engine idles at the desired speed. Check synchronization by listening at each air intake in turn for any variation in the hiss, using a piece of rubber tubing. The larger the throttle opening the louder the hiss.

When the sounds are equal, tighten the interconnecting shaft coupling so that the throttles work in unison. A final check should now be made on the mixture strength by lifting each piston in turn, making any fine adjustments to the jet adjusting nuts which may be required to balance it.

Float adjustment on the HS1

If there has been trouble with flooding and the needle and seating are clean, check the fuel level in the float chamber. This can be done by the method shown in **FIG 2:25**. Use a piece of $\frac{7}{16}$-in-diameter bar between the forked lever and the float lid. With the needle on its seating the fork should just rest on the bar. To adjust this setting, bend the lever at the point indicated.

Modified 'Sprite' I damper assembly

To allow the carburetter pistons to lift more freely and avoid restriction of performance, a modified damper assembly was introduced. The damper pistons were shortened from .378 in to .308 in. The later assemblies are identified by the letter 'O' stamped on the brass hexagon caps. They can be fitted, with advantage, to earlier carburetters in pairs.

Faulty performance

If there is trouble on the road it may be due to a piston sticking, to a blocked jet or to flooding. Check the piston by removing the air cleaner and the piston damper, and then lifting the piston with a finger. It should rise and fall freely. If it does not, the trouble may be dirt or a badly centred jet. A blocked jet may sometimes be cleared by opening the throttle with the engine running and momentarily blocking the air intake. With the throttle still open the engine should start to race, showing that the jet has been cleared. Flooding from the float chamber may be due to dirt in the needle valve. The needle can be removed by withdrawing the float pivot pin. If the tapered end of the needle is deeply grooved, replace both needle and seating with new ones. If there is apparently a lack of fuel, disconnect the pipe to the carburetter and if the pump is working there should be regular spurts of fuel from the pipe.

Air cleaners for SU carburetters

With the exception of the 'pancake' type fitted to 'Sprites' I, these are of the dry-type. To clean the 'Sprite' I air cleaners remove the units and wash the gauze in fuel every 3000 miles. When the gauze is dry again, re-oil with engine oil, allow to drain and refit.

Do not disturb the dry-type element until a replacement is needed. To renew the element, unscrew the wing nut on the top and prise off the cover. Extract the old element and clean out the inside of the container before fitting the new element. Position the air intake adjacent to the exhaust manifold in cold weather, moving it away in the summer.

On 'Sprites' II and III and 'Midgets' I and II, disconnect the breather pipe and remove the centre nut and washer from the tie bracket. Unscrew the through-bolts and lift off the air cleaners so that the elements can be renewed.

FAULT DIAGNOSIS

Leakage or insufficient fuel delivered

1 Air vent in tank restricted
2 Petrol pipes blocked
3 Air leaks at pipe connections
4 Pump or carburetter filters clogged
5 Pump gaskets faulty
6 Pump diaphragm damaged
7 Pump valves sticking or seating badly
8 Fuel vapourising in pipelines due to heat

Excessive fuel consumption

1 Carburetters need adjusting
2 Fuel leakage
3 Sticking controls
4 Dirty air cleaners

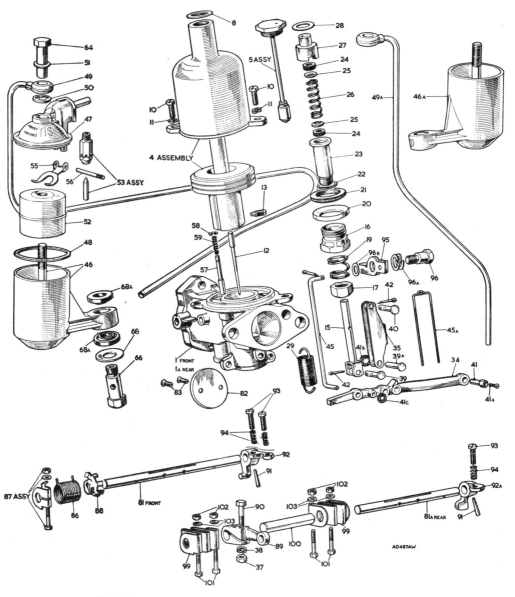

Fig 2:23 Components of the SU carburetters, type H.1, fitted to 'Sprite I'

Key to Fig 2:23 1 Body—bare—front. 1A Body—bare—rear. 4 Suction chamber and piston assembly.
5 Oil damper assembly. 8 Fibre washer—oil damper cap. 10 Securing screw—suction chamber. 11 Spring washer—
D/C—screw. 12 Jet needle. 13 Jet needle locking screw. 15 Jet with head. 16 Jet sealing nut. 17 Jet adjusting nut.
19 Jet adjusting lock spring. 20 Jet sealing ring—brass. 21 Jet sealing ring—cork. 22 Jet bearing copper washer—
bottom half bearing. 23 Jet bearing—bottom half. 24 Jet gland washer—cork. 25 Jet gland washer—brass.
26 Jet gland spring. 27 Jet bearing—top half. 28 Jet bearing copper washer—top half bearing. 29 Jet return spring.
34 Jet lever. 35 Jet link. 37 Nut (2BA). 38 Washer. 39 Pivot pin—short. 39A Pivot pin—jet link.
41 Pivot pin—jet lever to stirrup. 41A Screw—cable clamp. 41B Starlock washer—jet link. 41C Starlock washer—link rod.
42 Split pin. 45 Link rod. 45A Stirrup—connecting jet lever. 46 Float-chamber—bare—front. 46A Float-chamber—
bare—rear. 47 Float-chamber lid. 48 Float-chamber lid washer. 49 Overflow pipe—front. 49A Overflow pipe—rear.
50 Serrated fibre washer—cap nut. 51 Aluminium packing washer. 52 Float. 53 Float needle and seat assembly.
55 Float hinged lever. 56 Float hinged lever pin. 64 Cap nut—float lid. 66 Holding-up bolt—float-chamber.
68 Washer—steel—holding-up bolt. 81 Throttle spindle—front. 81A Throttle spindle—rear. 82 Throttle disc.
83 Throttle disc screw. 86 Return spring—throttle—front. 87 End clip. 88 Anchor plate. 89 Throttle lever.
90 Bolt (2BA). 91 Taper pin. 92 Throttle stop—front. 92A Throttle stop—rear. 93 Adjusting screw.
94 Lock spring—screw. 95 Rocker lever—front. 96 Bolt—pivot—front. 96A Spring washer—pivot bolt.
96B Aluminium washer—cam. 99 Coupling—folded. 100 Connecting-rod—throttle. 101 Bolt (4BA).
102 Nut (4BA). 103 Washer (4BA).

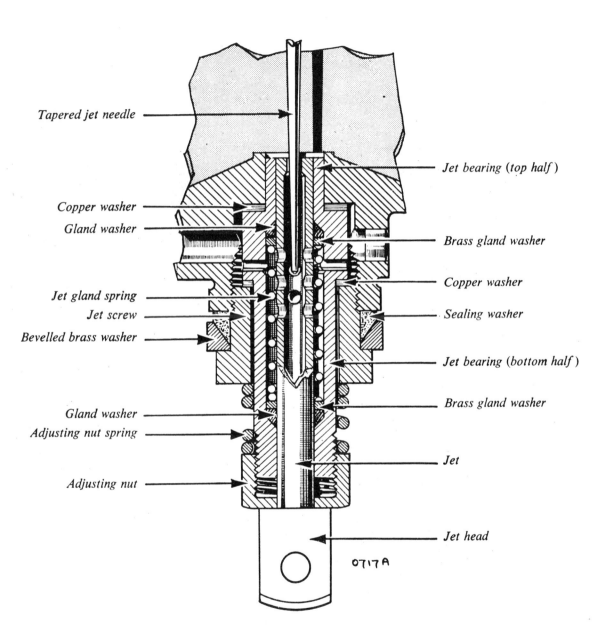

Tapered jet needle

Copper washer

Gland washer

Jet gland spring

Jet screw

Bevelled brass washer

Gland washer

Adjusting nut spring

Adjusting nut

Jet bearing (top half)

Brass gland washer

Copper washer

Sealing washer

Jet bearing (bottom half)

Brass gland washer

Jet

Jet head

0717A

Fig 2 : 24 Sectioned jet assembly on the SU carburetter, type H.1. Note the jet sealing glands at each end of the spring

5 Excessive engine temperature
6 Brakes binding
7 Tyres under-inflated
8 Idling speed too high
9 Car overloaded

Idling speed too high

1 Rich fuel mixture
2 Carburetter controls sticking
3 Slow-running screws incorrectly adjusted
4 Worn carburetter throttle valve

Noisy fuel pump

1 Loose mountings
2 Air leaks on suction side and at diaphragm
3 Obstruction in fuel pipe
4 Clogged pump filter

No fuel delivery

1 Float needle stuck
2 Vent in tank blocked
3 Electric pump connections faulty
4 Electric pump contacts dirty
5 Pipeline obstructed
6 Pump diaphragm stiff or damaged
7 Inlet valve in pump stuck open
8 Bad air leak on suction side

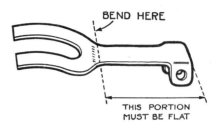

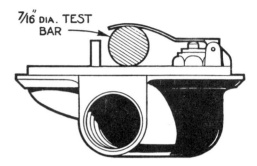

Fig 2:25 Checking and adjusting the float lever on 'Sprite I' carburetters

CHAPTER 3

THE IGNITION SYSTEM

Automatic timing   Routine maintenance   Removing   Dismantling   Servicing
Assembling   Installing   Timing   Faulty performance   Sparking plugs
Fault diagnosis

All the cars covered by this manual have distributors which incorporate automatic ignition timing, both by a centrifugal mechanism and vacuum control. The weights of the centrifugal device fly out against the tension of small springs as the engine speed rises. This movement advances the contact breaker cams relative to the distributor driving shaft, giving advanced ignition according to engine speed. The vacuum control is operated by the depression in the inlet manifold, this suction varying with engine load. At small throttle openings with no load on the engine there is a high degree of vacuum in the manifold, causing the control on the distributor to advance the ignition. When hill-climbing on large throttle openings the much-reduced vacuum means that the control will retard the ignition. The units mentioned can be seen in **FIG 3:1**.

Routine maintenance

With the rotor removed, add a few drops of oil to the cam bearing. This is point 3 in **FIG 3:2**. Do not remove the screw.

Smear the cams with a small amount of grease or a very little engine oil. Squirt a few drops of oil into the gap between the cams and the contact breaker plate, taking care that no oil gets on the plate or near the contacts. Adjust the contact breaker points by turning the engine until they are fully opened by one of the cams, as shown in **FIG 3:2**. Slacken screw 1 and with a screwdriver in slots 2, move the fixed contact plate until the gap between the points is between .014 in and .016 in. Set the sparking plug gaps to an opening between .024 in and .026 in.

Removing the distributor

1 Turn the engine by hand until the rotor arm points to No. 1 plug lead in the distributor cap. Note the position of the vacuum unit as it will simplify connecting the vacuum pipe during assembly.
2 With the low-tension lead disconnected from its terminal, and the suction pipe from the vacuum control unit, remove the two bolts securing the clamp plate to the distributor housing. This plate 3 can be seen in **FIG 3:5** where the pinch bolt 5 is also clearly shown. Do not slacken this pinch bolt or the ignition timing will be lost.

Dismantling

1 To remove the contact breaker assembly, complete with plate, lift off the rotor and withdraw the slotted low-tension terminal post shown at top right in **FIG 3:1**. Remove the two screws securing the plate to the distributor body, ease up the plate and unhook the vacuum link.
2 Dismantle the contact breaker assembly by removing the nut and washer from the anchor pin for the moving contact spring. Now withdraw the insulating bush and the tags, noting the order and position so that they will be correctly replaced. Lift off the moving contact and the insulating washers from the anchor and pivot pins. The fixed contact plate is removed by unscrewing the single fixing screw, together with both the spring and flat washers.

Remove the securing screw to release the capacitor.

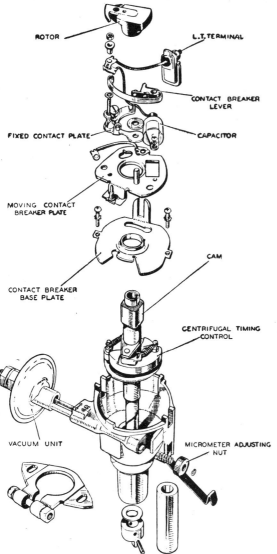

ROTOR

L.T. TERMINAL

CONTACT BREAKER LEVER

FIXED CONTACT PLATE

CAPACITOR

MOVING CONTACT BREAKER PLATE

CAM

CONTACT BREAKER BASE PLATE

CENTRIFUGAL TIMING CONTROL

VACUUM UNIT

MICROMETER ADJUSTING NUT

Fig 3:1   The component parts of the Lucas DM2 distributor

IMPORTANT

At the top, inside the spigot which locates the rotor arm, is a screw which must be removed in order to release the cam spindle. Before doing this, note the relative positions of the rotor arm driving slot and the driving dog at the bottom of the spindle, see **FIG 3:1**. This is to ensure that the timing is not 180 degs out when the cam spindle is re-engaged with the centrifugal weights during assembly.

3 Having removed the cam spindle, take off the centrifugal weights, each one being an assembly complete with spring and toggle.

4 To unscrew the milled adjusting nut and the spring from the vacuum unit spindle, remove the circlip at the extreme end. Now withdraw the unit.

5 To remove the driving spindle from the body, drive out the parallel pin which secures the driving dog. Note the position of any thrust washers.

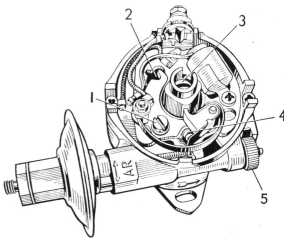

Fig 3:2   Distributor cap removed to show the contact breaker platform.

Key to Fig 3:2   1 Contact adjusting screw.   2 Contact adjusting slot.   3 Cam and drive shaft oiling point.   4 Contact points.   5 Micrometer adjuster.

Servicing

Examine the distributor cap for cracks or signs of 'tracking'. Evidence of the latter can be seen as a thin black line between the brass segments inside the cap. The only cure is to replace the cap with a new one.

The carbon brush 1 in **FIG 3:9** should protrude slightly and move freely. It is of composite construction to give some degree of radio interference suppression, the top part being a resistive compound. Never replace this long type with a short, non-resistive brush. Clean the cap thoroughly with a dry cloth. Renew the rotor if the metal electrode is loose or badly eroded.

The faces of the contact breaker points should be clean, with a greyish, frosted look. If not too deeply burned and pitted, they can be polished by using a fine stone with a rotary motion. It is essential to keep the faces flat and square, so that they meet perfectly when fitted. Clean afterwards with petrol. The movable contact arm should be free on its pivot without being unduly slack. If there is wear of the centrifugal timing weights and pivot pins renew the weights and the cam assembly. The latter must also be renewed if it is not a close sliding fit in the driving shaft. Excessive clearance causes cam wear and erratic opening of the contact points. Check the fit of the driving shaft in the body and renew the shaft and the bearings if they are worn. Immerse new bushes in thin engine oil for twenty-four hours, or for two hours in oil heated to 100°C. They can then be pressed into the distributor body.

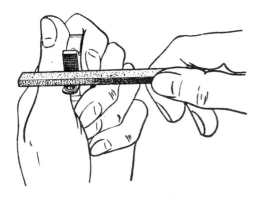

Fig 3:3   Cleaning the contact breaker points

3 Insert the driving spindle into the distributor housing in the crankcase so that it meshes with the camshaft gear. When it is fully home, the slot must be at twenty minutes past ten with the small offset below and to the left. This position is clearly shown by the inset in **FIG 3:5**. The driving dog on the distributor is also offset and will mesh only in one place.

On 'Sprite' I

Follow the previous instructions but replace the spindle with the offset slot in the position shown in **FIG 3:6**. The screwed rod should be $\frac{5}{16}$ in UNF. On 948 and 1098 cc A35's and A40's, on 'Sprites' II and III and 'Midgets' I and II, again follow the original instructions but replace the spindle with the offset slot at twenty minutes to two with the large offset uppermost as in **FIG 3:7**. The screwed rod should be $\frac{5}{16}$ in UNF.

The distributor can now be replaced.

Assembling

1 Lubricate, with thin engine oil, the parts of the centrifugal advance mechanism, the drive shaft and the section of the shaft where the cam fits.
2 Assemble the parts, making sure that the cam driving pins engage with the centrifugal weights in the original position. When seen from above, the small offset of the driving dog must be on the right when the driving slot for the rotor arm is at six o'clock.
3 When replacing the vacuum control unit, turn the adjusting nut to the half-way position.
4 Adjust the contact breaker to the correct gap.

Installing

1 Insert the distributor in the engine housing and turn the rotor until the driving dogs engage. Being offset, there is only one position for the dogs where this can take place.
2 Fit the two bolts securing the clamp plate and tighten them after setting the vacuum control unit to the position it occupied originally.
3 Fit the vacuum pipe and distributor cap and check the timing.

NOTE

Leave one of the bolts holding the clamp plate to the distributor housing slack, until the pinch bolt has been tightened. If the pinch bolt rotates in a fixed nut, tighten to 50 lb/in. If the bolt is tightened by a rotating nut, use a torque figure of 30 lb/in.

Setting the driving spindle

The distributor is driven by a spindle which engages with a skew gear on the camshaft. If this spindle has been removed according to the instructions given in the Engine Chapter, it must be accurately replaced or the ignition timing will be out.

On 800 cc A30's

1 Screw a length of $\frac{5}{16}$ in BSF rod, or a long bolt, into the end of the driving spindle, as shown in **FIG 3:4**.
2 Turn the crankshaft until No. 1 piston is at tdc on the compression stroke. Valves 7 and 8 will then be just rocking.

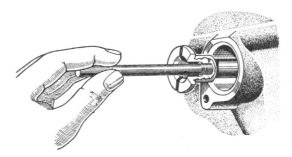

Fig 3:4   Using a piece of threaded rod to replace the distributor driving spindle

Timing the ignition

On A30's before engine No. 93536, the timing marks on the flywheel are not visible unless the gearbox is removed. To time the ignition without seeing the marks proceed as follows.
1 Set No. 1 piston at tdc on the compression stroke with valves 7 and 8 just rocking.
2 Slacken the distributor clamp bolt and turn the distributor body until the contact points are just about to open with the rotor pointing to No. 1 plug lead segment in the distributor cap.
3 Tighten the clamp bolt, replace the cap and test on the road.

With low octane fuel the engine should pink slightly under load in top gear from 10 mph to 30 mph with the accelerator hard down. If pinking is violent and persists after 30 mph the ignition must be retarded by small movements of the micrometer adjusting knob. If there is no pinking or it dies out early, advance the ignition.

With premium fuel there will be no pinking and the flywheel marks must be used. Turn the crankshaft to set No. 1 piston at tdc as before.
1 Turn the flywheel until the $\frac{1}{4}$ mark lines up with the pointer on the housing.
2 Turn the flywheel backwards so that the 1/4 mark is $\frac{33}{64}$ in away from the pointer, corresponding to $6\frac{1}{2}$ degs of crankshaft rotation. This is the setting for fuels rated at less than 80 octane. With premium fuels set the mark $\frac{7}{8}$ in away, corresponding to 11 degs of rotation.

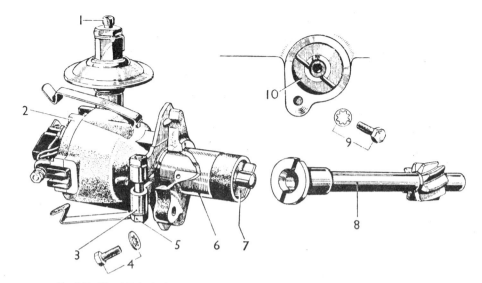

Fig 3:5   The A30 body, housing and drive shaft. The inset shows the offset slot in shaft

Key to Fig 3:5   1 Vacuum unit.   2 Distributor body.   3 Distributor clamp.   4 and 9 Securing screws and washers.
5 Clamp bolt.   6 Housing.   7 Driving key.   8 Drive shaft.   10 Driving dog.

3 Slacken the distributor bolt, point the rotor at No. 1 segment in the cap, then turn the distributor until the points are just opening.

4 Tighten the clamp bolt and test on the road, making slight adjustments on the micrometer knob if necessary.

Timing on later A30's and all other models

1 Set No. 1 piston at tdc on the compression stroke.

2 Turn the crankshaft until the recess in the crankshaft pulley flange is in line with the longest pointer on the timing case cover. This is marked tdc in **FIG 3:8**. If the timing cover is off, align the timing marks on the camshaft and crankshaft wheels.

3 Turn the crankshaft backwards to obtain the correct angular setting in degrees btdc as given in Technical Data.

4 Set the micrometer adjustment in the central position, turn the distributor body until the contact points are just opening with the rotor arm pointing at No. 1 plug lead segment in the cap.

5 Tighten the clamp plate bolt.

It is possible to use the electrical method to determine the precise moment when the contact points open. To do this, remove the vacuum pipe and turn the distributor body until the contact points are fully closed. Turn on the ignition switch, remembering that the low-tension lead must be connected to the distributor. Connect a twelve-volt lamp with one lead to the low-tension terminal and the other to earth and rotate the distributor body clockwise until the lamp lights. This is the position where the points have just opened. Now tighten the clamp bolt, check that the rotor is opposite No. 1 plug lead segment in the cap, refit the cap and vacuum pipe and test on the road. The micrometer adjustment is used for small movements only, and is intended to set the timing accurately for slightly different grades of fuel.

The adjustment nut is shown by the lower arrow in **FIG**

3:10. Turn it clockwise to retard and anti-clockwise to advance the ignition, looking on the end of the threaded spindle. Each graduation at the point shown by the upper arrow represents an approximate timing movement of 5 degs. This is equal to 55 clicks on the adjusting nut.

Timing with a stroboscopic lamp

1 Disconnect the vacuum pipe.

2 Do not allow the engine rev/min to rise higher than 600 or the centrifugal weights in the distributor will advance the ignition.

Fig 3:6   The offset of the distributor drive in the correct position for 'Sprite I'

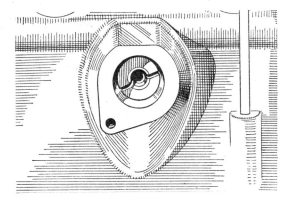

Fig 3:7 Correct position of driving slot with large offset uppermost. This applies to all models except the A30 and 'Sprite I'

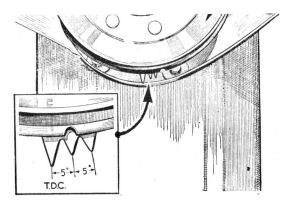

Fig 3:8 The ignition timing pointers. Note the notch in the pulley rim

Faulty performance

Misfiring and difficult starting may be due to defective high-tension leads to the plugs and ignition coil. To renew them, remove the securing screws inside the distributor cap, as shown in **FIG 3:9**. Fill the holes in the cap with silicone grease and push the leads into place so that there is a ring of grease to form a water-tight seal. Secure the leads with the pointed screw. Press carbon brush 1 to see that it moves freely. Replace the cap and leads so that the firing order is 1, 3, 4, 2, bearing in mind that the rotor moves anti-clockwise. Start the engine, and if misfiring is evident and it is known that it is not due to other defects in the engine, disconnect each plug lead in turn and hold it about $\frac{3}{16}$ in away from the cylinder head. If the spark is strong and regular, but misfiring continues when the lead is replaced, then the sparking plug is at fault. The treatment of sparking plugs is dealt with in a later section. If the spark from the lead is weak and irregular, suspect the distributor or the low-tension circuit. If the distributor, and the contact breaker points, are in good condition, test the low-tension circuit with a 20-volt voltmeter.

1 Switch on the ignition and turn the crankshaft until the points are fully open.
2 Check battery to starter switch cable. Connect voltmeter between the supply terminal of starter switch and earth. No reading indicates a faulty cable or connection.
3 Check cable from starter switch to fuse unit terminal 'A1'. Connect voltmeter between terminal 'A1' and earth. No reading indicates a faulty cable or connection.
4 Check control box. Connect voltmeter between control box terminal 'A1' and earth. No reading indicates a faulty control box.
5 Check cable from control box to lighting and ignition switch. Connect voltmeter between the lighting switch terminal 'A' and earth. No reading indicates a faulty cable or connection.
6 Check the ignition switch. Connect the voltmeter between the switch and earth. No reading indicates a faulty switch.
7 Check cable from ignition switch to fuse unit terminal 'A3'. Connect voltmeter between terminal 'A3' and earth. No reading indicates a faulty cable or connection.

8 Check cable from fuse unit terminal 'A3' to ignition coil. Connect the voltmeter between the ignition coil terminal SW and earth. No reading indicates a faulty cable or loose connection.
9 Check the ignition coil. Connect the voltmeter between the ignition coil terminal CB and earth. No reading indicates a faulty ignition coil.
10 Check cable from ignition coil to distributor. Connect the voltmeter between the distributor terminal and earth. No reading indicates a faulty cable or connection.
11 Check the distributor. Connect the voltmeter across the contact points. If there is no reading, remove the capacitor and test again. If there is then a reading, the capacitor is at fault. Test the capacitor by substitution, connecting a new one between the low-tension terminal and earth. Fit a new capacitor complete with bracket, but if the capacitor alone is available, unsolder the old one from its bracket, using as little heat as possible when soldering the new one. The capacity is 0.2 microfarad.

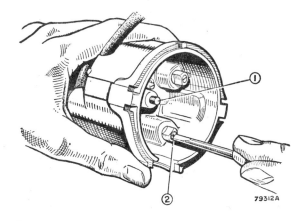

Fig 3:9 Connecting the high-tension leads. 1 is the carbon brush, 2 is the cable-securing screw

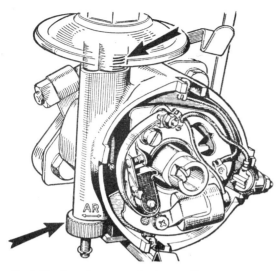

Fig 3:10 The micrometer adjusting nut. The vernier scale is shown by the top arrow

A final test is to remove the high-tension lead from the centre of the distributor cap. Switch on the ignition and turn the crankshaft until the contact points are closed. Hold the high-tension cable about $\frac{3}{16}$ in away from the cylinder block and flick the contact breaker lever to open the points. If there is a strong spark the ignition coil is in order, but no spark indicates a faulty coil.

Sparking plugs

Examine the deposits on the firing end to check on working conditions. The normal condition will be for a plug which is of the correct grade used for a mixed period of high- and low-speed driving. This leaves a deposit which is from brown to greyish tan in colour. White to yellowish powdery deposits indicate long periods of constant-speed driving or much low-speed city driving. Neither of these deposits will affect performance if the plugs are cleaned on a blasting machine and the gaps reset. File the sparking surfaces to reveal bright clean metal.

Wet black deposits can be traced to oil fouling, due mainly to cylinder bore wear, or worn pistons, rings and valve stems.

Dry, fluffy black deposits are caused by rich mixture or misfiring. Excessive idling or slow speeds will also keep plug temperatures so low that normal deposits are not burned off.

A white blistered appearance of the insulator nose, and badly eroded electrodes, indicate over-heating. This can be caused by weak mixture, poor cooling, incorrect ignition timing or sustained high speeds and heavy loads.

After cleaning, which should include the sparking plug threads, set the gap between the electrodes to a figure between .024 and .026 in. Fit new gaskets and tighten to a torque of 30 lb/ft. If the plugs cannot be seated by hand, clean out the threads in the cylinder head by using a tap or an old sparking plug with three or four saw cuts down the threads.

Replacement sparking plugs must be those specified by the car manufacturers, and the correct types will be found in Technical Data.

FAULT DIAGNOSIS

Engine will not fire

1 Battery discharged.
2 Distributor contact points dirty, pitted or out of adjustment.
3 Distributor cap dirty, cracked or 'tracking'.
4 Carbon brush inside distributor cap not in contact with rotor.
5 Faulty cable or loose connection in low-tension circuit.
6 Distributor rotor arm cracked.
7 Faulty coil.
8 Broken contact breaker spring.
9 Contact points stuck open.

Engine misfires

1 Distributor contact points dirty, pitted or out of adjustment.
2 Weak contact breaker spring.
3 Distributor cap dirty, cracked or 'tracked'.
4 Faulty coil.
5 Faulty cable or loose connection in low-tension circuit.
6 High-tension plug and ignition coil leads cracked or perished.
7 Sparking plug loose.
8 Sparking plug insulation cracked.
9 Sparking plug gap incorrect.
10 Ignition timing too far advanced.

CHAPTER 4

THE COOLING SYSTEM

Operation   Maintenance   Water pump   Thermostat   Temperature gauge
Anti-freeze   Fault diagnosis

All the cars described in this manual have pressurized water cooling systems in which the natural thermo-syphon circulation is augmented by a centrifugal impeller mounted at the rear end of the fan spindle. This impeller receives water from the bottom tank of the radiator and passes it through the cylinder block. It then goes up into the cylinder head until it reaches a thermostat at the front end of the head. The thermostat valve remains closed while the water is cold, so that the water re-circulates round the engine and warms up rapidly. This rapid warm-up reduces the risk of severe cylinder bore wear. When the water reaches a temperature in the region of 80°C the thermostat valve opens, allowing the water to pass through the top hose into the radiator header tank. From here the hot water falls through the radiator core to the bottom tank, being cooled on its way by the external air flow through the core. The volume of cooling air is increased by a belt-driven fan.

A spring-loaded valve in the filler cap pressurizes the cooling system and so raises the temperature at which the water boils. **FIG 4:1** shows the cap removed, and the locking cams on the filler spout. When the engine is hot, unscrew the cap slowly until the resistance of the lobes at the ends of the cams can be felt. After waiting a moment until the pressure is released, the cap can be removed.

Maintenance

Overheating may be caused by a slack fan belt. With the correct tension it should be possible to move the belt laterally about 1 in at the centre of its longest run. To adjust the belt refer to **FIG 4:2** which shows the three nuts to be slackened. Lift the generator by hand, tighten the adjusting link nut first, followed by the other two, and finally check the tension. A belt which is too tight throws an undue strain on both generator and fan spindle bearings.

The bearings in the water pump rarely need replenishment, being packed with grease, but if it is thought necessary some extra lubricant can be introduced through the large screw hole above point 'A' in **FIG 4:3**. Do not use pressure or the lubricant may reach the carbon seal and impair its efficiency. To drain the radiator and water passages, open the tap beneath the radiator and the tap at the rear of the cylinder block, as seen in **FIG 4:4**. Anti-freeze can be collected, strained and used again, but if topping up with water is needed, remember that this dilution will reduce the protection. If the car is fitted with a heater, draining the engine and radiator will not drain the heater unit so that anti-freeze must be used. This should be of the ethylene glycol or glycerine type conforming to Specification B.S. 3151 or B.S. 3152.

The water system should be flushed periodically to clear away the sludge and deposits which tend to clog the passages. Remove the filler cap, open the drain taps and flush the system with clean water from a hose held in the filler orifice. Extra cleaning can be given by removing the radiator, turning it upside down and flushing it through in the reverse direction. When re-filling, close the drain taps, open the water tap to the heater if one is fitted and fill slowly, using soft water for preference.

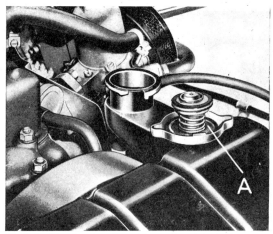

Fig 4:1   Showing the radiator filler cap A and the locking cams on the spout

Water pump

The water pump fitted to early A30's is shown in **FIG 4:5**. The water seal is readily dismantled but the rear bearing needs a special tool to centralise it because it must pass through the front bearing housing on its way out. This needs the services of a well-equipped garage.

To dismantle as far as this proceed as follows.

1 Remove the radiator and slacken the top clip of the thermostat by-pass hose. This is the hose clipped to the by-pass tube 8.
2 Remove the generator as detailed in the Electrical Chapter.
3 Unscrew the four nuts holding the pump body to the cylinder block and remove the pump with the by-pass hose.
4 Remove the fan blades and the fan pulley (when detachable) from the hub.
5 Remove the spindle nut and washer and withdraw the hub. Prise out the Woodruff key 21.
6 Hold the pump body and tap out the spindle towards the rear, using a soft-faced hammer. The spindle will carry with it the impeller vane and water seal assembly, items 16 to 20. Note that parts numbered 1 to 6 and 14 and 15 are assembled and removed from the front end of the body.
7 Prise out the spring retaining ring 6 and remove the lubricant retainer 5. Bearing 4 and distance piece 3 can then be tapped out from the rear by a drift, but the rear bearing needs a special tool to remove it, as mentioned earlier.

Examine the bearings and the carbon sealing ring 16 for wear. Renew worn parts and the spring 19 if it has weakened.

Reassemble in the reverse order. After engine No. 41992 a modified seal assembly was fitted. This one-piece seal replaces items 16, 18 and 19 in the earlier water pump. The complete pump assembly is interchangeable with the old one, but the pump body 7, the water seal assembly, the distance piece 17, the spindle with vane 20 and the lubricant retainer 5 are not separately interchangeable.

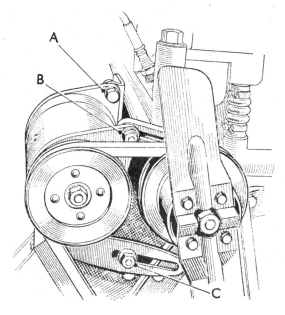

Fig 4:2   To adjust the fan belt loosen generator nuts A and B and link nut C

Water pump, all other models

This can be seen in section in **FIG 4:3**. It is removed from the engine according to the previous instructions and can then be dismantled.

1 Remove the fan blades and belt pulley from the hub.
2 The hub is an interference fit on the shaft and must be pulled off with an extractor.
3 Pull out the bearing locating wire through the hole in the top of the pump body just in front of point 'A'.
4 Tap the spindle gently rearwards, releasing the combined spindle and bearing assembly, with seal and vane.
5 The impeller vane is an interference fit on the spindle and can be drawn off with an extractor, enabling the one-piece water seal assembly to be removed.

Check the spindle and bearing assembly for wear. The bearings cannot be replaced if worn, so that the whole spindle assembly must be renewed. Also replace the seal if the carbon face is worn or if there is evidence of leakage. When reassembling in the reverse order make certain that the hole in the bearing body is in line with the lubricating hole 'A' before pressing the spindle and bearing assembly into the pump housing. Note when fitting the vane that the tips of the blades must clear the body by the dimension given in **FIG 4:3**. If the interference fit of the fan hub was impaired when it was removed from the spindle, the hub should be renewed. Take care that the face of the hub is flush with the end of the spindle as shown at point 'B' in **FIG 4 : 3**.

If the original spindle and bearing assembly has been retained and it is thought advisable to introduce some extra lubricant, do so through the screw hole above point 'A' in **FIG 4 : 3**. Do not exert undue pressure when doing this or lubricant may be forced past the seals. Fit the fan and pump assembly to the cylinder block using a new paper joint washer, and after replacing the generator and belt, adjust the latter to the correct tension.

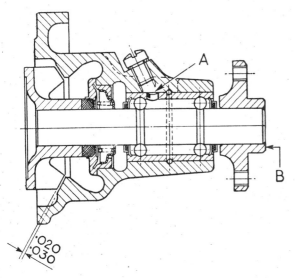

Fig 4 : 3 Sectioned water pump of later type showing lubricating hole in bearing assembly at A

Thermostat

1 To remove the thermostat drain the cooling system and remove the top hose from the outlet elbow at the front end of the cylinder head.
2 Take off the three securing nuts and spring washers and lift the elbow from the studs.
3 Remove the paper joint washer and lift out the thermostat.
4 Test the thermostat opening temperature by immersing it in hot water to the temperature given in Technical Data. If the valve does not start to open or is stuck in the fully open position, renew it, as it cannot be repaired.

Installation is the reverse of removal, but see that the joint washers are in good condition. One of them will be found in a recess in the cylinder head, under the thermostat flange.

In an emergency the engine can be run with the thermostat removed.

Temperature gauge

On all the 'Sprite' and 'Midget' cars a temperature gauge unit is fitted. This consists of a thermal element in the radiator header tank, connected to a dial indicator in the instrument panel by means of a capillary tube filled with mercury. Nothing can be done either to the tube or to the instruments if there is a failure of any kind. Replacement then involves the element, the dial indicator and the tube complete. The combined water temperature and oil pressure gauges are of integral construction, and should one of these fail, both will have to be renewed.

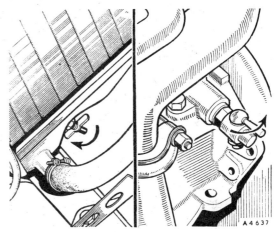

Fig 4 : 4 Radiator drain tap (left) and cylinder block drain tap (right). Arrow shows direction to open

Anti-freeze

The relatively high temperatures developed in a pressurized cooling system prevent the use of anti-freeze solutions having an alcohol base, because of their high evaporation rate. For this reason only ethylene glycol or glycerine types are suitable, as mentioned under 'Maintenance'. Before adding anti-freeze mixture, the radiator should be flushed through with a hose in the filler neck and the drain tap open.

Anti-freeze can remain in the system for two years if the specific gravity of the solution is checked periodically and fresh anti-freeze added as required. The anti-freeze manufacturer can supply the equipment needed for the specific gravity check. After the second winter, drain the system, flush out and refill with fresh water and anti-freeze if required.

Top up the radiator when the cooling system is at its normal running temperature to avoid losing anti-freeze by expansion.

The correct solutions of anti-freeze for different degrees of frost protection are given in the following table.

Solution %	Absolute safe limit	Commences freezing at
20	−19°C −3°F	−9°C 16°F
25	−26°C −15°F	−13°C 9°F
30	−33°C −28°F	−16°C 3°F

FAULT DIAGNOSIS

(a) Internal water leakage
1 Cracked cylinder wall
2 Loose cylinder head nuts
3 Cracked cylinder head
4 Faulty head gasket
5 Cracked tappet chest wall

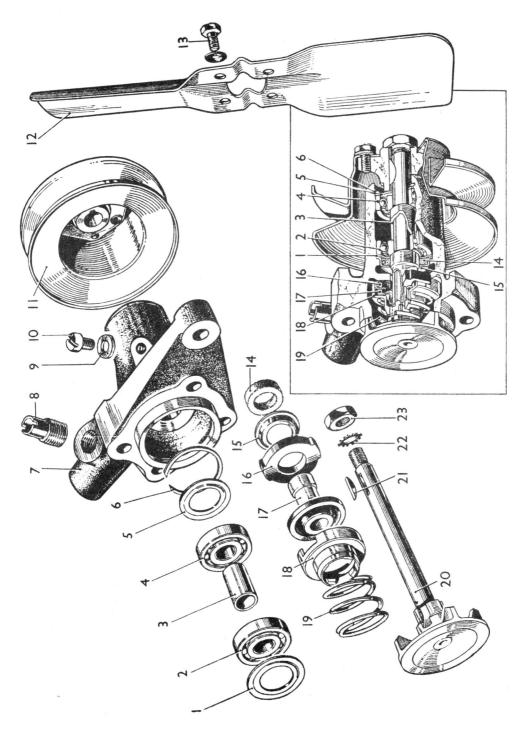

Fig 4:5   Early A30 water pump exploded

Key to Fig 4:5   1 Felt retainer, outer.   2 Bearing, rear.   3 Bearing distance piece.   4 Bearing, front.   5 Lubricant retainer.   6 Spring ring.   7 Pump body.
8 By-pass tube.   9 Screwed plug washer.   10 Screwed plug.   11 Fan and pump pulley.   12 Fan blade.   13 Setscrew and washer.   14 Felt ring.   15 Felt retainer, inner.
16 Sealing ring.   17 Rubber seal and distance piece.   18 Locating cup.   19 Gland spring.   20 Spindle with vane.   21 Woodruff key.   22 Shakeproof washer.
23 Nut for spindle.

(b) Poor circulation

1 Radiator core blocked
2 Engine water passages restricted
3 Low water level
4 Loose fan belt
5 Defective thermostat
6 Perished or collapsed radiator hoses

(c) Corrosion

1 Impurities in the water
2 Infrequent draining and flushing

(d) Overheating

1 Check 4, 5 and 6 in (b)
2 Sludge in crankcase
3 Faulty ignition timing
4 Low oil level in sump
5 Tight engine
6 Choked exhaust system
7 Binding brakes
8 Slipping clutch
9 Incorrect valve timing
10 Retarded ignition
11 Mixture too weak

CHAPTER 5

THE CLUTCH

Operation   Early clutch   Later clutch   Mechanical operation   Hydraulic operation
Slave cylinder   Hydraulic adjustment   Hydraulics — 'Sprites' and 'Midgets'   Fault diagnosis

The clutch is shown in section in **FIG 5:1**. This illustrates the type fitted to earlier cars, but the working principle is the same for the later type. The clutch has a single driven plate to which are riveted the friction linings 3. The hub of this plate slides on splines machined on the gearbox first-motion shaft, the drive from the plate to the hub being transmitted by springs to give a cushioned take-up. The plate is sandwiched between the rear face of the flywheel 1 and a spring-loaded pressure plate 18 carried inside a cover 4 which is bolted to the flywheel. The pressure plate can be drawn backwards against the power of the thrust springs 5 in order to free the driven plate and thus disengage the drive. This movement of the pressure plate is effected by a series of levers 12 and the release bearing 7 and 8. The release bearing derives its movement from levers connected to the clutch pedal either mechanically or hydraulically.

Servicing

The clutch cover is normally serviced as an assembly, complete with pressure plate, thrust springs and release levers. Expensive tools and gauging equipment are needed to assemble and adjust the cover accurately, and it is work best left to a competent agent.

Early-type clutch

The following instructions will cover the clutches fitted to early A30 and A35 cars, and to the 948 cc A40's, 'Sprites' and 'Midgets'.

To remove the clutch, take off the gearbox as detailed in Chapter Six.

1 Slacken the clutch cover screws a turn at a time, working diagonally until the spring pressure is relieved, and then remove entirely.
2 The driven plate will then be completely free and should be examined for the following faults. If the plate can be used again do not touch the linings with cleaning fluids.

Looking at **FIG 5:2**, the splines in the hub 11 must not be worn nor the edges of the flange which engages the springs 10. The springs should not be broken, neither should they be weakened so that they are free to rattle. Now examine the linings for excessive wear, loose rivets, cracks and discolouration. The polished glaze is quite normal and does not affect the ability to transmit power, but the linings should be light in colour, with the grain of the material quite clearly visible through the glaze. Evidence of oil on the linings can be seen in the much darker colour and a glazed deposit on the surface which has obliterated the grain. This will cause two defects; the clutch will stick on engagement so that it is difficult to free and yet it will slip under load. Signs of oil on the clutch can be attributed to leakage past the rear main crankshaft bearing or from the gearbox. It is not advisable to rivet new linings to an old plate. The plate may be distorted, and there may be trouble with out-of-balance effects.

Now proceed to examine the pressure plate assembly. If the friction surface of the plate 8 is ridged or pitted the assembly should be renewed. This also applies to the machined surface of the release lever plate, where it contacts the carbon release bearing 16. This face must be smooth and there must be no ridge round the outer edge due to wear.

If there has been trouble such as slip or drag, and the pressure unit is suspected, then it can be checked by an agent with the proper equipment. If it is otherwise unworn the agent will be able to look for weak or broken springs and set the release levers accurately. Otherwise the only answer is to fit a replacement unit complete.

The release bearing 16 must have a smooth polished bearing surface, without signs of cracks or pitting. The carbon block must stand proud of the cup in which it is

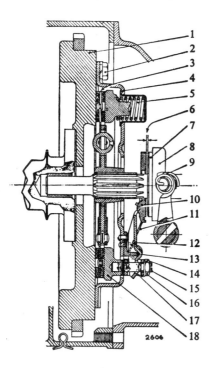

Fig 5:1 Section of the clutch fitted to 800 cc and 948 cc engines

Key to Fig 5:1 1 Flywheel. 2 Holding screw. 3 Driven plate. 4 Cover. 5 Thrust spring. 6 Clearance $\frac{1}{16}$ in. 7 Graphite release bearing. 8 Release bearing cup. 9 Release bearing carrier. 10 Release lever plate. 11 Lever retainer and anti-rattle spring. 12 Release lever. 13 Knife-edge fulcrum. 14 Tag lock washer. 15 Stud. 16 Adjusting nut. 17 Bearing plate. 18 Pressure plate.

housed by at least $\frac{1}{16}$ in. If less than this, both cup and bearing must be renewed. The clutch withdrawal lever 15 can be rebushed if necessary. Note that the A30 lever is much longer than the one illustrated, and that it has an eye in the end for the operating rod.

Refitting

First check the flywheel with a dial gauge for 'run-out'. If satisfactory, the clutch can be fitted, but it will be necessary to use a pilot mandrel to centralise the driven plate. The reason for this can be seen in **FIG 5:1**. Notice that the splined first motion shaft from the gearbox locates in a bush in the flanged end of the crankshaft. As it must pass through the driven plate hub to reach this bush it is evident that the two must be perfectly in line. This is done by using the Service tool shown in **FIG 5:3**.

1 Hold the clutch assembly on the flywheel and fit the bolts finger tight. Note that the longer boss to the driven plate hub has chamfered splines. These must face to the rear to facilitate entry of the first motion shaft splines.

2 Insert the Service tool 18G 139 through the clutch cover and the driven plate hub so that the pilot enters the spigot bearing in the end of the crankshaft. This will centralise the driven plate.

3 Tighten the clutch cover securing bolts a turn at a time in diagonal sequence to avoid distorting the cover.

4 Remove the Service tool, refit the gearbox and adjust the clutch pedal free travel. This operation is covered in a later section on withdrawal mechanisms.

Later-type clutch

This clutch is of larger diameter to transmit the extra power of the 1098 cc engines fitted to the later A35's, A40's, 'Sprites' and 'Midgets'.

FIG 5:4 shows the clutch in section, and an exploded view of the components can be seen in **FIG 5:5**. The hydraulic slave cylinder shown as operating the release lever in **FIG 5:4** will not be correct for the A35, which is fitted with a mechanical link to the clutch pedal.

As there is no fundamental difference between this clutch and the earlier type already covered, the instructions for dismantling and refitting remain the same.

Mechanical operation

The clutch pedal linkage on the A30 and A35 cars can be seen in **FIG 5:6**, which is a view looking towards the rear of the car. Dismantle and reassemble in the following manner.

1 Detach the pull-off spring 2 and the anti-rattle spring 6 if one is fitted. Then disconnect the operating rod 4 by removing the domed nut and locknut.

2 Remove the cotter which secures the pedal lever 1 to the shaft 5, by slackening the nut a few turns and knocking the cotter loose. This prevents damage to the cotter thread. The nut is then unscrewed. On later models the pedal is secured to the shaft by a locating screw and locknut.

3 Release the set screws in the support flanges of the clutch pedal shaft and knock out the peg in the outer spherical bush.

4 Drive the shaft through the pedal lever towards the gearbox, which operation will release the outer

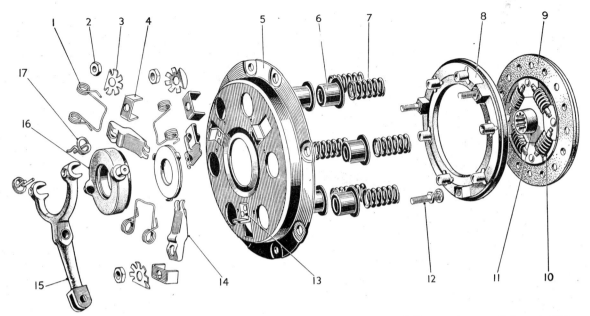

Fig 5:2 Components of the clutch fitted to early 800 cc and 948 cc engines

Key to Fig 5:2 1 Anti-rattle spring. 2 Adjusting nut. 3 Tab washers. 4 Bearing plates. 5 Clutch cover.

6 Flanged cups. 7 Thrust springs. 8 Pressure plate. 9 Clutch driven plate. 10 Driven plate springs. 11 Splined hub. 12 Shoulder stud. 13 Fulcrum. 14 Release lever. 15 Clutch withdrawal lever. 16 Release bearing and cup assembly. 17 Retaining spring.

spherical bush and flanges. The shaft can then be withdrawn from the supporting boss on the gearbox, together with the inner bush and flange.

Examine the shaft and bushes for wear, renewing them if necessary. Also renew stretched springs and the rubber gaiter round the withdrawal lever if it is perished. Note that from chassis No. 13675 the inner Oilite bush was changed for a brass-lined rubber one.

To reassemble the parts, fit the shaft with the inner flange and bush and feed it into the gearbox boss. Now fit it with the outer bearing flange and pin the outer spherical bush to the shaft. Draw the shaft outwards until the outer support flanges can be bolted together. The pedal lever can then be refitted, and the inner bearing flange bolted up, finally hooking on the springs and adjusting the pedal clearance.

Adjusting mechanical linkage

Press the clutch pedal with one finger, depressing it until resistance is felt. The pedal should depress and return quite freely, with a movement of no more than $\frac{3}{8}$ in for the early clutch and $\frac{5}{8}$ in for the later type. To adjust this clearance slacken the lock nut at the forward end of the operating rod 4 and turn the larger nut until the clearance is correct. Lock the nuts together when all is correct. Excessive pedal clearance will make it difficult to disengage the clutch, and insufficient clearance will cause clutch slip.

Hydraulic operation on A40

This method of operating the clutch ensures a smooth take-up by eliminating the effect of flexibly mounted engines upon more rigid mechanical linkages. **FIG 5:7**

shows the master cylinder piston 6 which is operated by the suspended clutch pedal 15. Pressure on the piston forces hydraulic fluid through tubing to a slave cylinder on the clutch housing. This cylinder, which is shown in section in **FIG 5:8** and can be seen at the lowest point in **FIG 5:4,** copies the movement of the master cylinder piston.

Being coupled to the clutch release lever, the slave piston will therefore pass on the pedal movement to the release bearing and so disengage the clutch. The tube between the slave cylinder and the chassis is flexible so that engine movement has no effect on the operating fluid.

Dismantling

1 Push the hooked ends of return spring 13 off the pedal arms, remove circlip 11 and withdraw shaft 10 until the pedals are free.
2 Remove circlip 16 from pin 9 and pull out the pin.
3 Disconnect the pressure pipe union from the end plug 2, remove the securing nuts from the flange bolts and lift off the master cylinder.

To inspect the internal parts of the cylinder do the following.

1 Remove the filler cap 26 and drain out the fluid. Peel back the rubber boot 18 and remove circlip 8 from inside the cylinder mouth.
2 Invert the cylinder and tap it on a wooden surface to remove the inner assembly. This consists of the pushrod and stop washer 7, the piston 6 and secondary cup 19 together, the piston washer 5, the main cup 20 and the spring retainer 21 with return spring 22. Item 23 is not used in the clutch master cylinder.

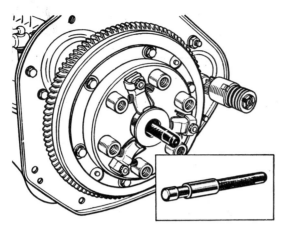

Fig 5:3 Centralising the driven plate. The Service Tool shown is 18G 139

3 Remove the secondary cup by stretching it over the piston with the fingers. The external metal parts can be cleaned with normal liquids, but the components inside the cylinder must not be cleaned with anything but hydraulic fluid. Examine the parts for wear, especially the cups. If there is any doubt at all about the cups it is essential to renew them.

Before reassembling be certain that everything is spotlessly clean. Then lubricate the parts with the correct hydraulic fluid and assemble them in the order shown in **FIG 5:7**.

The clutch slave cylinder, A40, all 'Sprites' and 'Midgets'

The cylinder is shown in section in **FIG 5:8**. It comprises the body 5, fitted with a push-rod 8, a rubber boot 7, a circlip 6, a piston 4, the rubber cup 3 with cup filler 2 and spring 1. There is also a bleed screw not shown.

Dismantling

Remove the pipe union from the cylinder, using a clean tin to catch the fluid. Take out the clevis pin connecting the push-rod to the clutch withdrawal lever, remove the bolts holding the cylinder to the clutch housing and lift away.

1 Remove the rubber boot 7, the push-rod 8 and the circlip 6.

2 It is easiest to blow out the piston 4, the cup 3 and associated components by using a compressed air supply on the pipe union hole.

The instructions for cleaning and reassembling are the same as those for the master cylinder. Disturbance of either the master cylinder or the slave cylinder means that the fluid system must be bled free from air.

Bleeding—all models

Fill the master cylinder reservoir with the correct hydraulic fluid. Attach a rubber tube to the slave cylinder bleed valve and immerse the open end in a small volume of the fluid in a clean glass jar.

With somebody to pump the clutch pedal, open the bleed screw on the slave cylinder about three-quarters of a

turn. At the end of each down stroke of the clutch pedal close the bleed screw before allowing the pedal to return. At first there will be air bubbles appearing in the fluid in the jar, but the pumping operation must be repeated until clear fluid free from bubbles is delivered.

It is important to maintain the fluid level in the reservoir at all times and particularly while the system is being bled, as fluid is then being drawn from the reservoir in quantity. If all the fluid is used, air can enter the master cylinder bore through the small feed hole to be seen in the floor of the reservoir and this will nullify all previous work on bleeding the system.

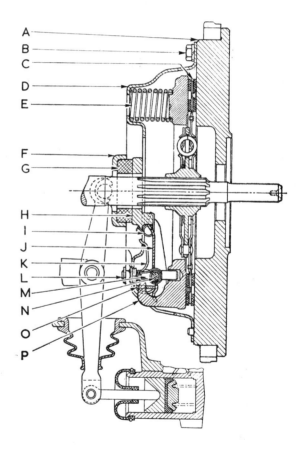

Fig 5:4 Section of the later clutch fitted to the 1098 cc engines. The slave cylinder is shown at the bottom

Key to Fig 5:4 A Flywheel. B Securing bolt. C Driven plate. D Clutch cover. E Thrust coil spring. F Release bearing cup. G Graphite release bearing. H Release plate. I Lever retainer spring. J Release lever. K Anti-rattle spring. L Adjusting nut. M Eyebolt. N Floating pin (release lever). O Strut. P Pressure plate.

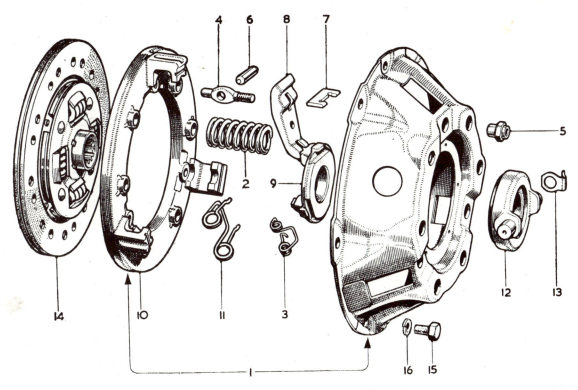

Fig 5:5 Components of the clutch fitted to 1098 cc engines

Key to Fig 5:5 1 Clutch assembly.   2 Thrust spring.   3 Release lever retainer.   4 Eyebolt.   5 Eyebolt nut.
6 Release lever pin.   7 Strut.   8 Release lever.   9 Bearing thrust plate.   10 Pressure plate.   11 Anti-rattle spring.
12 Release bearing.   13 Retainer.   14 Driven plate assembly.   15 Clutch to flywheel screw.   16 Spring washer.

Adjusting hydraulic operation

The correct amount of free movement between the master cylinder push-rod and the piston is set during manufacture, and should not need alteration. If the adjustment has been disturbed, reset the effective length of the push-rod by slackening the locknut and turning the rod by the hexagon provided. Depress the pedal pad gently until resistance is felt and adjust the push-rod until the distance required to reach this point is approximately $\frac{5}{32}$ in. This ensures that the push-rod has a minimum free movement of $\frac{1}{32}$ in before the master cylinder piston starts to move. There is no provision for adjustment on A40's.

Hydraulic clutch—'Sprites' and 'Midgets'

The slave cylinder is identical with that described in the A40 section. The master cylinders for operating the clutch and brakes are, however, contained in a common casting with a fluid reservoir serving both bores, see **FIG 5:9**. The top row of parts is for the clutch cylinder, the items numbered 7, 8 and 9 being used for the brake cylinder only. This arrangement of cylinders does not affect the working principle, which is the same as that described for the A40.

Dismantling

The master cylinder unit can be withdrawn complete with pedals. It is most important, before removing it, to check which bore is used for operating the clutch so that the pipes can be connected the right way round during assembly.

1 Remove the heater by disconnecting the electrical leads and then releasing the blower bracket from the bulkhead.
2 Unscrew the ten set screws holding the master cylinder mounting plate to the bulkhead.
3 Disconnect the two hydraulic pipes from the rear of the master cylinder unit and withdraw the unit upwards, manipulating the pedals through the hole in the bulkhead.
4 Disconnect each pedal from the master cylinder by removing the clevis pins from the push-rod forks.
5 The unit is fixed to the mounting plate by two bolts, nuts and washers. When these are unscrewed the unit is free.

The instructions for stripping down, cleaning and assembling are the same as those given for the A40, but the following details should be noted.

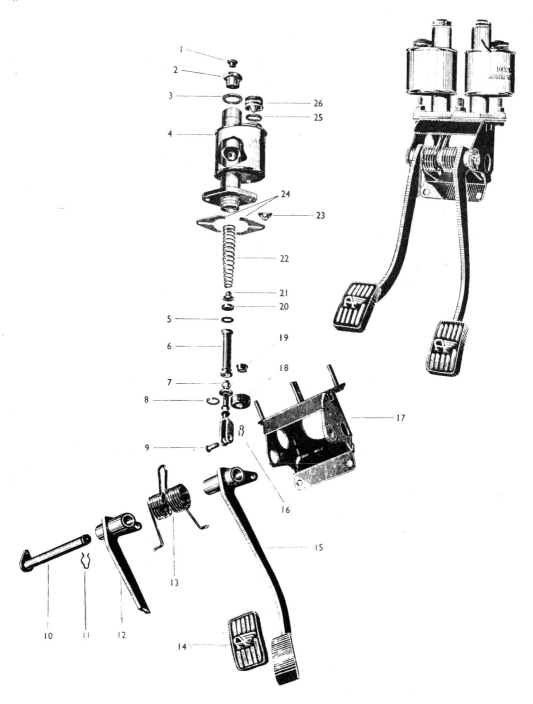

Fig 5:7   A40 clutch master cylinder exploded

Key to Fig 5:7   1 Rubber plug (replaced by outlet union when fitted to vehicle).   2 End plug.   3 Washer.   4 Supply tank.
5 Piston washer.   6 Piston.   7 Push rod.   8 Circlip.   9 Clevis pin.   10 Pedal cross-shaft.   11 Circlip.   12 Pedal arm.
13 Return spring.   14 Pedal rubber.   15 Pedal arm.   16 Circlip.   17 Mounting bracket.   18 Rubber boot.   19 Secondary cup.
20 Main cup.   21 Spring retainer.   22 Return spring.   23 Not applicable in this installation.   24 Packing pieces.   25 Washer.
26 Filler cap.

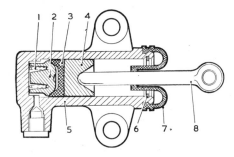

Fig 5:8   Section of the slave cylinder

Key to Fig 5:8   1 Spring.   2 Cup filler.   3 Cup.   4 Piston.
5 Body.   6 Circlip.   7 Boot.   8 Push rod.

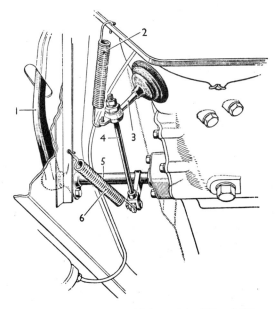

Fig 5:6   Clutch pedal linkage of the A30 and A35

Key to Fig 5:6   1 Clutch pedal lever.   2 Pull-off spring.
3 Clutch withdrawal lever.   4 Clutch operating rod.   5 Clutch
pedal shaft.   6 Anti-rattle spring (later models)

Assemble the retainer 11 on the smaller end of the
return spring 10. The main cup 12 is inserted with the lip
foremost. Be careful not to bend the lip backwards as it
enters. This also applies to the secondary cup 15, after it
has been fitted to the piston, using the fingers only.

When fitting the rubber boots 19, make sure that the
vent hole in each boot will be at the bottom when the unit
is replaced in the car. The boots fitted to the later 'Sprites'
and 'Midgets' differ in shape from those illustrated, but
this has no effect on the general instructions.

Fill the reservoir with clean hydraulic fluid of the correct
grade, and push the clutch cylinder piston inwards several
times, allowing it to return unassisted. Do this until fluid
flows from the outlet.

Installation of the unit is the reverse of the dismantling
procedure. Afterwards, bleed the system.

FAULT DIAGNOSIS

(a) Drag or spin

1 Oil or grease on the driven plate linings
2 Bent engine back plate
3 Misalignment between the engine and the first motion
   shaft
4 Leaking master cylinder or pipeline
5 Driven plate hub binding on first motion shaft
6 First motion shaft spigot binding in crankshaft bush
7 Distorted driven plate
8 Warped or damaged pressure plate or clutch cover
9 Broken driven plate linings
10 Dirt or foreign matter in clutch
11 Air in the clutch hydraulic system

(a) Fierceness or snatch

1 Check 1, 2, 3 and 4 in (a)
2 Worn clutch linings

(c) Slip

1 Check 1, 2 and 3 in (a)
2 Check 1 in (b)
3 Weak anti-rattle springs
4 Seized piston in clutch slave cylinder

(d) Judder

1 Check 1, 2 and 3 in (a)
2 Pressure plate not parallel with the flywheel face
3 Contact area of driven plate linings not evenly distributed
4 Bent first motion shaft
5 Buckled driven plate
6 Faulty engine or gearbox rubber mountings
7 Worn shackles
8 Weak rear springs
9 Loose propeller shaft bolts
10 Loose rear spring clips

(e) Rattle

1 Check 3 in (d)
2 Broken springs in driven plate
3 Worn release mechanism
4 Excessive backlash in transmission
5 Wear in transmission bearings
6 Release bearing loose on fork

(f) Tick or knock

1 Worn first motion shaft spigot or bush
2 Badly worn splines in driven plate hub
3 Release plate out of line
4 Faulty Bendix drive on starter
5 Loose flywheel

(g) Driven plate fracture

1 Check 2 and 3 in (a)
2 Drag and distortion due to hanging gearbox in plate
   hub

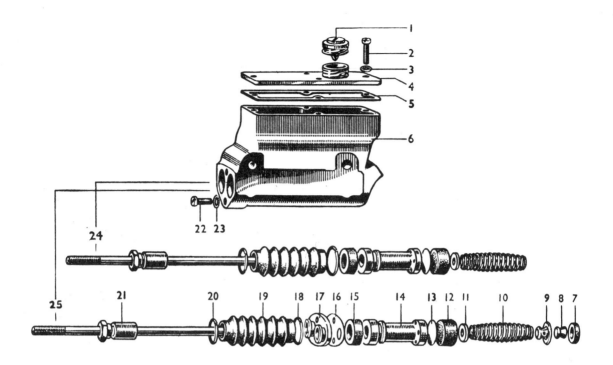

Fig 5:9 The 'Sprite I' master cylinders exploded. Parts 7, 8 and 9 are used in the brake bore only. Cylinders and parts for the later 'Sprites' and 'Midgets' differ only in minor details

Key to Fig 5:9 1 Filler cap.   2 Fixing screw.   3 Shakeproof washer.   4 Tank cover.   5 Tank cover gasket.
6 Cylinder barrel and tank.   7 Valve washer.   8 Valve cup.   9 Valve body.   10 Return spring.   11 Spring retainer.
12 Main cup.   13 Piston washer.   14 Piston.   15 Secondary cup.   16 Gasket.   17 Boot fixing plate.   18 Boot clip.
19 Boot.   20 Boot clip.   21 Push rod.   22 Fixing screw.   23 Shakeproof washer.   24 Clutch bore.   25 Brake bore.

CHAPTER 6

THE GEARBOX

Operation   Removing   Dismantling   Mainshaft   Laygear   Inspection
*   Reassembling   Modifications   Baulk rings   Fault diagnosis*

The gear-boxes fitted to all the cars covered by this manual are identical with two exceptions. The gear lever on the A30 and A35 operates directly on the selector rods, and there are needle roller bearings instead of plain bushes on the later 'Sprites' and 'Midgets'. The gearbox has four forward speeds and one reverse. Synchromesh engagement is incorporated on second, third and fourth gears. Top gear is a direct drive in which the first-motion shaft 4 in **FIG 6:1** is coupled to the third-motion shaft 6 and so to the propeller shaft.

The drive to the laygear 62 and to second and third-speed gears 16 and 20, is through single helical gears to ensure silent running. First-gear and reverse are selected by sliding the spur gears 25 and 45.

The third-motion shaft is extended well to the rear and carries the propeller shaft sliding joint on splines. Metal-to-metal cone clutches are used to facilitate gear changing by synchronizing the speeds of the coupling dogs. An internal cone can be seen at the left-hand end of part 16. The coupling dogs are shown internally in part II and in front of the gear teeth on part 16. The coupling sleeve 11 is spring loaded to the hub 12 by balls and springs so that when the sleeve is moved sideways by the shifting fork 31 it carries the hub with it until the cones engage. These speed up or slow down the coupling dogs until they are rotating at the same speed, the sleeve overcomes the resistance of the spring-loaded balls and further movement of the sleeve engages the dogs to complete the drive.

Lubrication

To reach the filler plug, remove the rubber plug on the left side of the gearbox covering. Fill with the correct grade of oil to the bottom of the threads. The drain plug is underneath the gearbox casing. Drain off the old oil when it is warm and examine it for metallic particles which may be a clue to excessive wear.

Removing

All the instructions needed to remove the engine and gearbox as a unit have been given in the Engine Chapter, but it is possible to remove the gearbox on the A30, A35 and A40 without taking out the engine, as follows.

1 Disconnect the battery, and the starter cable at the starter end.
2 Remove the distributor cap and leads, all electrical connections to the engine, and also the carburetter controls.
3 Drain the cooling system and detach the top hose and heater hoses from the engine.
4 Part the exhaust down pipe from the manifold.
5 From inside the car, lift off the rubber grommet round the gear lever and after removing the three set screws and spring washers, lift out the lever. On the A35 and A40 it will also be necessary to unscrew the top anti-rattle spring cap 7 in **FIG 6:2**. Take out the spring and plunger and after removing the gear lever collect the

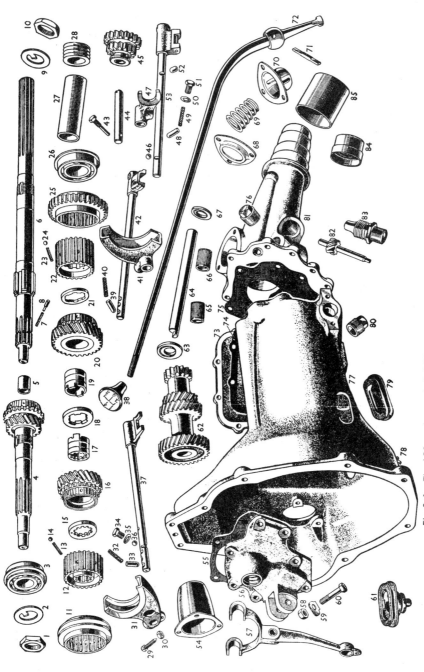

Fig 6:1 The A30 gearbox exploded. Most of the parts are identical for all other models

Key to Fig 6:1 1 1st motion shaft nut. 2 Lockwasher. 3 1st motion shaft bearing. 4 1st motion shaft. 5 Bush for 3rd motion shaft. 6 3rd motion shaft. 7 Locking peg spring. 8 Locking peg. 9 3rd motion shaft lockwasher. 10 3rd motion shaft nut. 11 Third- and fourth-speed coupling sleeve. 12 Third- and fourth-speed synchronizer. 13 Synchronizer coupling sleeve. 14 Synchronizer coupling sleeve ball. 15 Splined thrust washer, front. 16 Third-speed mainshaft gear and cone. 17 Third-speed mainshaft gear bush. 18 Interlocking ring for bushes. 19 Second-speed mainshaft gear bush. 20 Second-speed mainshaft gear and cone. 21 Splined thrust washer, rear. 22 Second-speed synchronizer. 23 Second-speed synchronizer spring. 24 Second-speed synchronizer ball. 25 First-speed wheel. 26 3rd motion shaft bearing. 27 Distance piece. 28 Speedometer wheel. 29 Fork locating screw. 30 Locknut. 31 Third- and fourth-speed fork. 32 Plunger spring. 33 Plunger. 34 Plug. 35 Washer. 36 Ball. 37 Third- and fourth-speed fork rod. 38 Change speed lever knob. 39 Plunger for rod. 40 Spring. 41 First- and second-speed fork. 42 First- and second-speed fork rod. 43 Reverse shaft locking screw. 44 Reverse shaft. 45 Reverse wheel. 46 Ball. 47 Reverse fork. 48 Interlock plunger. 49 Spring. 50 Washer. 51 Plug for spring. 52 Interlock plunger. 53 Reverse fork rod. 54 Starter pinion cover. 55 Front cover joint washer. 56 Front cover. 57 Clutch withdrawal lever. 58 Nut. 59 Lockwasher. 60 Bolt. 61 Withdrawal lever dust cover. 62 Laygear. 63 Thrust washer, front. 64 Layshaft. 65 Needle roller bearing. 66 Needle roller bearing. 67 Thrust washer, rear. 68 Change speed lever dust cover. 69 Reverse spring. 70 Change speed lever seat, bottom. 71 Change speed lever, peg. 72 Change speed lever. 73 Side cover. 74 Joint washer for side cover. 75 Joint washer for rear cover. 76 Filler plug. 77 Gearbox case. 78 Split pin for clutch drain hole. 79 Dust cover. 80 Drain plug. 81. Rear cover. 82 Speedometer pinion. 83 Speedometer pinion sleeve. 84 Oil seal assembly. 85 Dust cover.

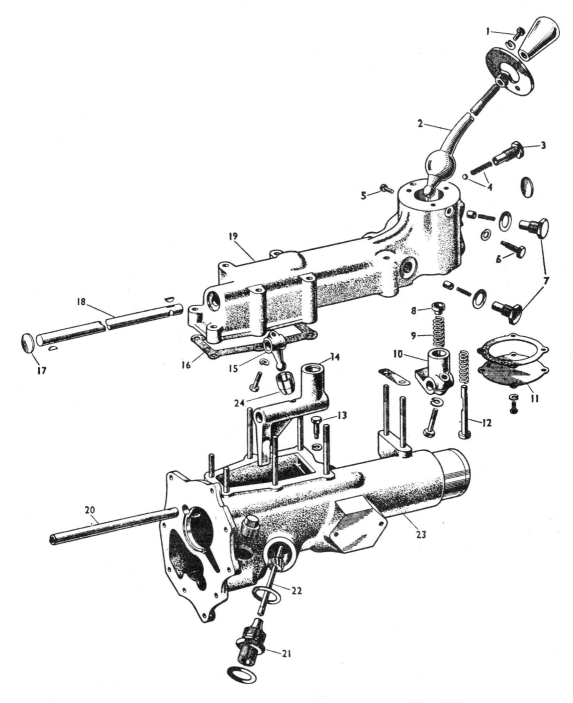

Fig 6:2 The remote gear control assembly fitted to all models except A30 and A35

Key to Fig 6:2 1 Change speed lever cover set-pin. 2 Change speed lever. 3 Reverse plunger cap. 4 Reverse plunger detent spring and ball. 5 Reverse plunger locating pin. 6 Change speed lever locating pin. 7 Anti-rattle spring caps. 8 Thrust button. 9 Thrust button spring. 10 Selector lever rear. 11 Bottom cover. 12 Reverse selector plunger. 13 Control shaft locating screw. 14 Control lever. 15 Selector lever front. 16 Joint washer. 17 Welch plug. 18 Remote control shaft. 19 Remote control housing. 20 Control shaft. 21 Speedometer pinion sleeve. 22 Speedometer pinion. 23 Gearbox rear cover. 24 Tapered bush.

thrust button 8 and spring 9.

6 Jack up the front of the car with the rear wheels raised on blocks to avoid damage to the exhaust pipe.

7 Uncouple the propeller shaft from the rear axle after marking the flanges.

8 On the A30 and A35, release the clutch pedal pull-off spring and remove the two nuts from the front end of the operating rod. On the A40 remove the slave cylinder instead.

9 Free the exhaust pipe and tie it to one side.

10 Disconnect the speedometer cable from the gearbox.

11 On the A30 and A35 release the two set screws in the inner, and the two nuts and bolts from the outer clutch pedal shaft support flanges, press out the pin in the outer spherical bush and slide the shaft away from the gearbox to free it.

12 Support the engine with a jack under the rear end of the sump.

13 On the A40, lift the carpets and take out the two set screws which pass through the transmission tunnel from inside the car, into the gearbox cross-member, releasing the cross-member from below. Do the same on the A30 and A35, removing the two set screws from the clamping plate under the gearbox rear cover.

14 Lower the jack so that the engine pivots on the front mountings until there is clearance for the bell-housing flange when drawn backwards.

15 Drain the gearbox and draw out the propeller shaft. See later important note for 'Sprite' I.

16 Remove the bolts and set screws from the bell-housing flange noting their positions. Remove the starter.

17 Pull the gearbox straight back until the first-motion shaft is clear of the clutch. Take the weight of the gearbox all the time. It must never be allowed to hang in the hub of the driven plate or the plate will be distorted with disastrous results on clutch operation.

18 Replacement is a simple reversal of the dismantling sequence, but if the clutch is disturbed it will be necessary to centralise the driven plate according to the instructions given in Chapter Five on the clutch. Do not forget the earthing strap between the bell-housing and the car body, making it a clean, tight connection.

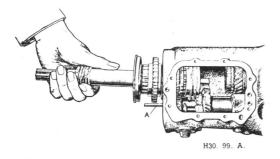

H30. 99. A.

Fig 6:3 Withdrawing the third motion shaft. The laygear is lowered on to dummy layshaft A

Removing—'Sprite' I

Follow the previous instructions with these exceptions.

1 The engine must be removed.

2 The gearbox can be lifted upwards out of the car.

3 It is most important *not* to detach the propeller shaft from the back end of the gearbox. Remove them together, and replace in the same manner.

Removing—'Sprites' II and III and 'Midgets' I and II

Again follow the initial instructions with these exceptions.

1 Remove the engine.

2 Lift the gearbox upwards out of the car. The propeller shaft can be left behind.

Dismantling

Remove the remote control assembly from the A35 and A40, 'Sprite' and 'Midget' gearboxes in the following manner, referring to **FIG 6:2** for details.

1 Remove the eight nuts securing the remote control housing 19 and lift off.

2 Unscrew the nine set screws and spring washers to release the rear cover 23 from the gearbox.

3 Pull the rear cover back slightly and turn it in an anti-clockwise direction viewed from the rear. This enables the control lever 14 to clear the fork rod ends and allow the rear cover to be removed.

4 Remove the control shaft locating screw 13 and screw it into the tapped front end of the control shaft 20. Slight pressure on the screw will enable the shaft to be removed, the control lever 14 slipping off the end.

5 Remove the bottom cover 11, then unscrew the locating pin 6. Shake out the anti-rattle springs and plungers after unscrewing the caps 7.

6 Release the set screws in the front and rear selector levers 15 and 10. Remove the welch plugs 17 at each end of the housing and drift out the shaft 18. Take care of the Woodruff keys.

7 The circlip round the front selector bush 24 is removed and the bush halves will then fall apart.

8 To remove the reverse selector plunger 12 unscrew cap 3 and shake out the detent ball and spring 4.

From now on the instructions will cover the gearboxes on all the cars.

9 Referring to **FIG 6:1**, unscrew the speedometer pinion sleeve 83 from the left side of the gearbox rear cover 81. Collect the joint washer and remove the pinion 82.

10 Remove the clutch release bearing from the lever 57 by levering out the two retaining springs.

11 Remove the clutch withdrawal lever by unlocking the tab washer 59 and unscrewing nut 58. The bolt is screwed into the support bracket and is reached by a box spanner passed through the hole blanked off by dust cover 79.

12 Pull off the front cover 56 after removing the eight set screws or nuts. Take care of the paper joint and packing shim.

13 Remove the side cover 73 and tilt the gearbox until the two springs and plungers fall out of the holes in the front edge of the joint face.

14 Remove the two plugs near the bell-housing on the side-cover side of the gearbox. Each has a fibre washer,

and the lower plug covers the reverse plunger and spring. The other plug has a long shank and covers the interlock ball between two of the selector rods.

15 Select neutral by aligning the slots at the rear ends of selector rods 37, 42 and 53. With the side cover aperture upwards, unlock and remove the reverse-fork locating screw, locknut and shake-proof washer from the fork 47. These can be reached through the drain plug hole. Also remove the similar screws, nuts and washers from the other two forks 31 and 41.

16 Tap the 3rd and 4th-speed selector rod 37 from the front end and withdraw it rearwards. Do the same to the 1st and 2nd-speed rod 42 and the reverse rod 53. As the rods are drawn out remove the two interlock balls from the holes at the front of the gearbox case, and the double-ended plunger 52 from the rear end. The three forks may now be lifted out.

17 Tap the layshaft 64 out of the front of the gearbox with a soft drift. When the drift is removed the laygear 62 and the thrust washers 63 and 67 will drop to the bottom of the box.

18 Draw the mainshaft assembly rearwards out of the gearbox case, then insert a long soft metal drift through the main shaft opening in the rear of the casing and drive out the first motion shaft, see **FIGS 6:3** and **6:4**. The laygear cluster and the thrust washers may now be removed.

19 Take out the reverse shaft locking screw 43 and push on the slotted end of the shaft 44 with a screwdriver, turning at the same time until the shaft is free and the gears 45 can be removed.

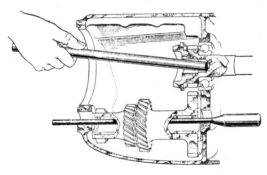

Fig 6:4 Drifting out the first motion shaft

Dismantling the mainshaft

1 Slide off the third- and fourth-gear synchronizer assembly and separate the coupling sleeve 11 by finger pressure. Wrap the assembly in a cloth during this operation to trap the three balls and springs 13 and 14 which will be released.

2 **FIG 6:5** will help the operator to follow the next step. Depress the small spring-loaded plunger C which locks the splined thrust washer D at the front end of the mainshaft. Turn the washer with a peg spanner until one of its splines holds down the plunger. Then slide the washer and third-speed gear off the shaft, removing the plunger and spring. Slide off the bush 17, the interlocking ring 18 and the second-gear 20.

3 Remove the splined rear thrust washer 21, and the first-speed wheel 25 with the second-speed synchronizer

assembly can be withdrawn off the end of the mainshaft. Separate the synchronizer as described in paragraph 1.

4 At the other end of the shaft unlock and remove nut 10 enabling the speedometer wheel 28 and the distance piece 27 to be removed. Draw off the ball bearing 26 in its housing and drift the bearing out.

Note that the reference to worn bushes in paragraph 2 will not apply to 'Sprites' II and III or to 'Midgets' I and II as their second- and third-speed gears run on needle rollers. When dismantling the third-motion shaft, remove the rear bearing and then withdraw the first-speed gear and synchronizer assembly. Depress the spring-loaded plunger which locks the rear splined ring at the back of the shaft. Turn the ring so that one of its splines covers the plunger and slide the ring off the shaft. Remove the plunger and spring and lift the two halves of the tabbed washer for the splined ring off the shaft. Slide the second-speed gear off the shaft, taking care to retain the needle rollers. Remove the third- and fourth-speed assemblies from the front end of the shaft in a similar manner.

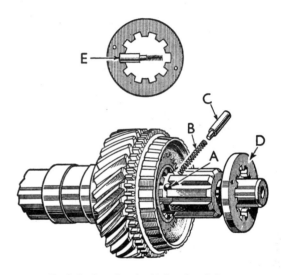

Fig 6:5 Securing the third motion shaft gears

Key to Fig 6:5 A Hole in shaft for locking plunger. B Spring. C Locking plunger. D Locking washer. E Locking washer with plunger engaged.

Dismantling the laygear

Twenty-three needle rollers are fitted into each end of the laygear. They are held in place by stepped races and spring rings as in **FIG 6:6**.

1 Remove the spring rings from each end and take out the rollers and inner and outer races.

2 Remove the inner spring rings and distance piece.

Inspection

The first- and third-motion shaft bearings 3 and 26 become worn after long service. Try to rock the outer races sideways and if there is any looseness the bearings must be renewed.

The synchronizer cones will also be worn after much use, and this is evident if gear changing has become noisy, with none of the usual resistance to gear lever

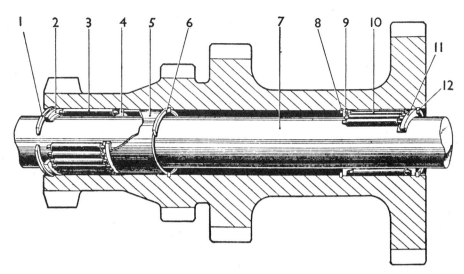

Fig 6:6 Section through laygear showing needle roller bearing assemblies

Key to Fig 6:6   1 Spring ring (outer).*   2 Outer race.*   3 Needle rollers.*   4 Inner race.*   5 Distance piece.*
6 Spring ring (inner).*   7 Layshaft.*   8 Spring ring (inner).**   9 Inner race.**   10 Needle rollers.**   11 Outer race.**
12 Spring ring (outer).**   * Small end.   ** Large end.

movement which shows that the cones are working. Replacement of the gear and cone assembly is then called for.

The third-motion shaft bush 5 is fitted inside the rear end of the first-motion shaft and should have a running clearance of .002 to .003 in with the spigot on the third-motion shaft. Excessive clearance may need renewal of the bush and possibly the shaft. The second- and third-speed gear bushes 17 and 19 have an extremely low tolerance of .0025 to .0015 in with the shaft. If there is any appreciable wear between these bushes and the third-motion shaft, they must be renewed.

Reassembling the mainshaft

The first-speed wheel 25 and the third- and fourth-speed coupling sleeve 11 are lapped in with their synchronizers and only mated pairs should be fitted. The hub splines of both synchronizers are also lapped with the mainshaft. Consequently, if an odd synchromesh assembly or mainshaft is fitted, it must be lapped with the part(s) concerned.

1 There is a spring ring on the outer race of the third-motion shaft bearing 26. Press the bearing into the housing (not illustrated) with the spring ring and the larger diameter of the housing on the same face. With the spring ring to the rear, press the bearing on to the mainshaft, fit the distance piece 27, the lock washer 9 and the nut 10. Tighten the nut securely and lock.

2 When assembling the first-speed wheel 25 to the second-speed synchronizer 22, ensure that the side of the wheel with the chamfered teeth faces towards the second-speed mainshaft gear 20 when assembled on the mainshaft. With some assistance, replace the three sets of springs and balls into the synchronizer 22 and fit the first-speed wheel. Push this assembly on to the mainshaft with the protruding boss of the synchronizer towards the bearing. Follow up with thrust washer 21.

3 Next fit the bush 19 with its legs away from the thrust washer and slide the second-speed gear 20 over the bush with its cone to the rear. Oil all the parts liberally during assembly. Locate the bronze interlocking ring 18 on the legs of bush 19 and mate the legs of bush 17 in the other pair of splines in the locking ring.

The order of assembly is different when dealing with 'Sprites' II and III and 'Midgets' I and II, because the bushes are replaced by needle rollers. Do not press the rear bearing on to the mainshaft until the following parts have been fitted. Working from the rear end of the mainshaft, assemble the second-speed gear, sticking the needle rollers in place with grease. Place the two halves of the washer for the splined ring on the shaft behind the second-speed gear, and ensure that the tabs are correctly located when fitting the ring. This is done after putting the spring and plunger into the hole in the mainshaft. The first-speed gear and synchronizer can be replaced with the protruding boss of the synchronizer to the rear. The bearing and housing may now be fitted, with the large-diameter flange of the housing to the rear. Refit the distance piece, speedometer gear, plain washer, lock washer and nut.

From the opposite end of the shaft, assemble the needle-roller bearing and fit the third-speed gear assembly. Place the spring and plunger in the hole in the shaft and refit the splined ring. Slide the third- and fourth-speed synchronizer on to the shaft with the boss on the hub away from the splined ring.

To resume the assembling sequence on the other cars, do the following.

4 Place the spring and plunger 7 and 8 in the hole in the mainshaft, depress the plunger and draw the third-speed mainshaft bush 17 slightly forward to keep the plunger depressed. Then slide the third-speed mainshaft gear 16 on to the bush with its cone away from the interlocking ring. Fit the steel thrust washer 15,

pushing it on as far as it will go. Slip a tube over the shaft and lightly tap the washer, turning it until the plunger is released and locks it.

5 Slide the third- and fourth-speed synchronizer assembly 11 and 12 on to the shaft with the boss on the hub away from the thrust washer.

Reassembling the laygear

1 Press the spring ring into the small end of the laygear, following it with the distance piece, which is drifted right home against the ring.

2 Assemble the needle roller bearings in the order shown in **FIG 6:6**.

Reassembling the first-motion shaft

1 A new self-lubricating bush can be fitted inside the gear end of the shaft by driving it in with a drift. The later 'Sprites' and 'Midgets' use a needle roller bearing here instead of a bush.

2 If the bearing 3 has been removed from the shaft, refit it with the spring ring away from the geared end.

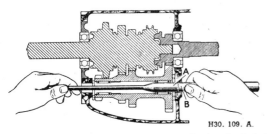

H30. 109. A.

Fig 6:7 Lifting the laygear into position. Dummy layshaft A pilots actual layshaft B

Reassembling the gearbox

1 Replace the reverse gear 45, aligning the hole in the shaft 44 with the hole in the casing and locking with screw 43 fitted with a spring washer.

2 **FIG 6:7** shows the use of a dummy layshaft, which is Service tool 18G471. This makes fitting the layshaft easier, but in the absence of such a tool it might be possible to fashion a similar device from a piece of wooden dowel rod. Insert the thin end of the dummy shaft through the clutch housing and place the large thrust washer 63 on it. Fit the laygear with the large end forward and as the dummy shaft emerges slip on the small thrust washer 67. The laygear must now have an end float between .001 and .003 in. Various small thrust washers are available to give the required end float, their thicknesses going up in .001 in steps from .125 in to .131 in. Let the laygear hang on the thin part of the dummy shaft.

3 Insert the third-motion shaft into the back end of the gearbox and drift the bearing housing into its recess until the flange is flush.

4 Turn the gearbox about until the laygear teeth are clear of the first-motion shaft housing and then drift the shaft into position from inside the clutch housing. The spring ring on the bearing must register properly in the recess.

5 Draw the dummy layshaft rearwards slightly and lift the laygears into mesh. Oil the layshaft and push it into place keeping contact with the dummy shaft all the way so that the thrust washers do not drop out of place.

6 Put the reverse fork 47 in position with its tapped hole facing the drain plug hole. Fit the fork 41 over the first-speed wheel 25, and the fork 31 over the third- and

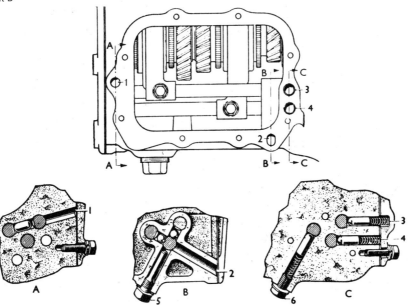

Fig 6:8 Location of balls and plungers

Key to Fig 6:8 1 Hole for interlock plunger between reverse and 1st and 2nd speed fork rods. 2 Hole for ball between reverse and 3rd and 4th speed fork rods. 3 Hole for 1st and 2nd speed fork rod plunger. 4 Hole for 3rd and 4th speed fork rod plunger. 5 Plug for 1st and 2nd, and 3rd and 4th speed ball hole. 6 Plug for reverse plunger hole. A, B and C are scrap views of sections AA, BB and CC respectively, looking in the direction of the arrows.

fourth-speed coupling sleeve 11.

7 With the side cover uppermost, push the reverse fork rod 53 through the lowest hole in the back of the gearbox casing, through the reverse fork and then through the clearance hole in the fork 31. Align the hole in the reverse fork with the hole in the rod and fit the locking screw through the drain plug hole, using the nut and shakeproof washer to lock the screw when tight.

8 Using **FIG 6:8** as a guide, drop the double-ended plunger 52 into the hole 1. Push the first- and second-speed fork rod 42 through the uppermost hole in the back of the casing, through the fork and into the front of the casing, locking the fork to the rod with the screw as before.

9 Fork rod 37 goes into the third hole, through the fork 31 until it just enters the hole in the front of the gearbox casing. Drop a ball down hole 2 in the side cover joint face. See that it goes between the reverse rod 53 and third and fourth fork rod 37 by looking from the clutch housing end. Using a piece of rod down hole 2, press hard on the ball to centralise the slot in the selector rod. If this is not done the ball will be in the way when the third and fourth fork rod is pushed home.

Turn the gearbox so that the drain plug is uppermost and drop a ball into hole 5 which will be in line with the drain plug hole. See that it goes between the first and second rod 42, and the third and fourth fork rod 37. Centralise the slot in the same way and push the third and fourth fork rod home, locking it in position. If an obstruction prevents the rods from being pushed right in, do not use a hammer but check that the balls are seating correctly in their slots. The correctly assembled position is shown in **FIG 6:9**.

10 Put the reverse plunger 48 into the lower hole on the drain plug side with the rounded end foremost, follow it with the spring and screw in the plug 51 fitted with a fibre washer, see position 6 in **FIG 6:8**. The upper hole is blocked by the long-shanked plug and fibre washer shown in position 5. Positions 3 and 4 show the holes in the side cover joint face which take the two remaining plungers 33 and 39 which are inserted with the rounded ends first. Follow up with the springs.

11 Replace the side cover and its paper joint washer using the eight nuts and spring washers, or the set screws used on early gearboxes. Tighten evenly by diagonal selection.

12 Position the front cover joint washer 55, and stick the packing shim into the front cover bearing recess with grease. Secure the cover with the seven nuts and spring washers.

Note: Although a .006-in shim is normally sufficient, use the following method to shim both front and rear covers 56 and 81. Measure the depth of the cover recess and the amount by which the bearing outer race protrudes from the gearbox casing. Tighten the cover with only the paper joint washer in place. Take off the cover and measure the thickness of the compressed paper washer. Add this thickness to the depth of the cover recess and subtract the amount by which the bearing protruded. The result gives the thickness of shims required. They are available in various thicknesses, but use the least number to achieve the desired result.

13 Replace the clutch withdrawal lever 57, using a lock washer on the bolt. Insert the bolt from the left-hand side and screw it into the bracket until it is tight enough to eliminate side play in the lever. Lock the bolt with the nut and spring washer and then bend up the tab of the lockwasher. Fit the rubber dust cover 61 and press the flat cover 79 into the opposite hole.

14 Fit the rear cover 81 using a sound paper washer. Place a .006-in shim in the recess machined to accommodate the projecting part of the rear bearing, but use the method suggested in paragraph 12 to check for the correct thickness of shimming. The shims are available in thicknesses of .004, .006 and .010 in.

15 Replace the remote control assembly in the reverse order to the instructions given for dismantling, then flush the gearbox with flushing oil and replace the drain plug. Do not forget to fill with oil of the correct grade. On all the cars, the gear lever is replaced after the gearbox is refitted into the chassis.

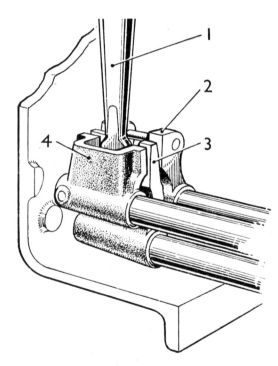

Fig 6:9 Position of selector rods

Key to Fig 6:9   1 Control lever.   2 Reverse rod.   3 Third and fourth speed rod.   4 First and second speed rod.

Modifications

The later type of third- and fourth-speed synchronizer 12 has three spring holes which are equally spaced, there are no lightening holes and the cone angles are altered. Interchangeability is affected as follows.

1 A new type third-motion shaft 6 can be used to replace an old one.

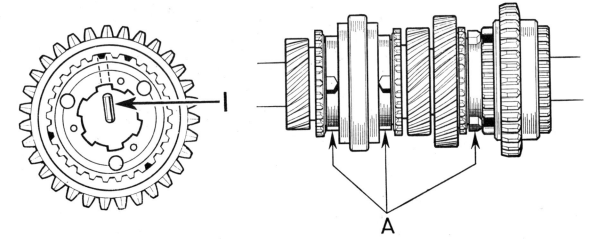

Fig 6:10 Correct position for first and second gear assembly and hub, 1098 cc cars

Fig 6:11   The mainshaft showing the baulk rings A. 1098 cc cars only

2 A new type second-speed mainshaft gear 20 with a new synchronizer 22 can replace their old counterparts, but they are not interchangeable separately.

3 A new type first-motion shaft 4 cannot be used to replace an old type, unless the following new parts are also fitted.
   (a) Third-motion shaft gear with cone 16.
   (b) Bush 17 for the third-speed mainshaft gear.
   (c) Third-motion shaft front thrust washer 15.
   (d) Third- and fourth-speed synchronizer 12.

New fork rods with modified notches can be interchanged with old ones in sets. Speedometer drive pinions of nylon were fitted on later gearboxes, and these are interchangeable with the original steel pinion and spindle. Nylon pinion bushes were also introduced in place of the brass bushes. The oil feed hole in the nylon bush is smaller to reduce the oil flow to the speedometer cable. When removing or replacing a nylon bush use a socket spanner to avoid damage to the hexagon. The copper sealing washer and the pinion oil seal retaining ring are not required with the nylon bush. Interchangeability is not affected.

Baulk rings

These are fitted to the second-, and to the third- and fourth-gear synchronizers on 1098 cc cars. The positions are clearly shown in **FIG 6:11**.

Note: If the first- and second-speed gear assembly has been dismantled it is most important to assemble the gear on the hub in the correct position, otherwise it will be impossible to select first gear. **FIG 6:10** shows the gear and hub correctly assembled with the plunger 1 aligned with the cut-away tooth in the gear assembly.

FAULT DIAGNOSIS

(a) Jumping out of gear

1 Broken change speed fork rod spring.
2 Excessively worn fork rod groove.
3 Worn coupling dogs.
4 Fork rod securing screw loose.

(b) Noisy gearbox

1 Insufficient oil.
2 Excessive endplay in laygear.
3 Damaged or worn bearings.
4 Damaged or worn teeth.

(c) Difficulty in engaging gear

1 Incorrect clutch pedal adjustment.
2 Worn synchromesh cones.

(d) Oil leaks

1 Damaged joint washers.
2 Damaged or worn oil seals.
3 Front, rear or side covers loose or faces damaged.

CHAPTER 7

PROPELLER SHAFT
REAR AXLE AND SUSPENSION

Universal joints   Dismantling joints   Rear axle   Axle shafts   Hub servicing
Servicing springs   Axle variations   Dampers   Servicing dampers   Modifications
Fault diagnosis

The front and rear universal joints on the propeller shaft are of Hardy-Spicer manufacture. The four journals on each spider run in needle roller bearings, as shown in **FIG 7:1**. The half coupling of the front joint is splined to the gearbox mainshaft and is free to slide. This accommodates the fore and aft movement of the propeller shaft as the rear springs deflect under road conditions and loading. Each spider journal has an inner shoulder which locates a metal retainer holding a cork sealing ring. The inner open ends of the bearing cups seal against the cork rings to prevent loss of lubricant and the ingress of dirt. These seals are marked 6 in the illustration.

Lubrication

Use the correct grade of grease when lubricating through the nipple fitted to each spider. Access to the front nipple is through a hole on the left side of the propeller shaft tunnel, normally closed by a rubber plug, but on later models by a metal plate with two screws. Oil from the gearbox lubricates the sliding splined joint. Smear the splines with oil when refitting the propeller shaft.

Removing

The joints can be tested for wear before removing the shaft. Try to lift each joint up and down. Slackness will indicate wear of the thrust faces on the spiders, and those inside the bearing cups. If the joints can be partially rotated it is a sign that the bearings are worn. Two pointers to trouble are often seen under the spring rings 7. A bright ring on the bearing cup shows that it has been rotating, and rust indicates a lack of grease.

After scribing a line across the flanges of the rear joint to ensure correct reassembly, separate them. Place a tray under the rear end of the gearbox to catch any oil which drains out, take the weight of the shaft and draw the front splines out of the box. On some of the cars it is easier to remove the shaft over the left-hand side of the rear axle.

Dismantling

Clean all dirt and enamel from the snap rings 7 and remove them by squeezing the ends together. Tap the yoke with a lead or copper hammer as shown in **FIG 7:2** when the top bearing cup should start to appear. Some support

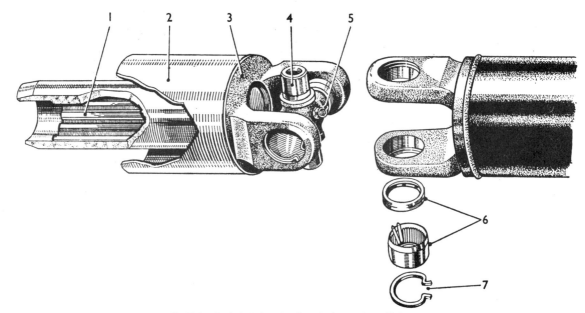

Fig 7:1 Exploded view showing the front universal joint

Key to Fig 7:1 1 Internal splined end of propeller shaft. 2 Dust cover. 3 Front half coupling. 4 Spider. 5 Nipple. 6 Needle bearing assembly. 7 Spring ring.

for the other yoke may help in this operation. If the bearing cup sticks it is permissible to tap on the inner lip of the cup if it is exposed, using a screwdriver or thin drift, but with the greatest care not to damage it. Pull the cup out vertically downwards to keep the rollers intact. Remove the opposite bearing, then the spider can be detached from the yoke. Repeat the operation on the remaining two bearings.

The spiders and bearings are available in sets. If the eyes in the yokes are worn oval, the bearing cups will no longer be a light drive fit, so that the yokes will need renewal.

Reassembling

It is advisable to renew the cork washers and retainers 6. Coat the shoulders on the spider journals with shellac and press the retainers into position with a tubular drift. Fill the holes in the spider with grease and insert in the yoke. Stick the needles in a bearing cup with vaseline, fill with grease and tap the cup into position using a soft drift slightly smaller in diameter than the yoke eye. Fit the spring ring and repeat the bearing assembly on the other side. If the spider appears to bind, tap the yoke lightly with a soft-faced mallet after the spring rings are fitted.

Refitting the completed shaft is a reversal of the removing procedure, but clean the rear flange faces and the register thoroughly. Line up the marks previously made on the flange edges and tighten the securing bolts diagonally and evenly.

The rear axle

FIG 7:3 shows the axle cut away to expose the internal mechanism. From this it can be seen that the bevel pinion is carried in a pair of taper roller bearings, with an oil seal immediately behind the universal joint flange. The large flange integral with the outer end of the axle shaft is bolted to a hub carried on a large ball-bearing which is also backed by a seal to prevent loss of lubricant. Note that the inner splined ends of the shafts engage with splines in the hubs of the two driven gears in the differential cage. When both axles are pulled out, the whole gear assembly can be withdrawn from the banjo casing by unscrewing the ring of nuts on the housing flange. At this point it would be as well to point out that there is very little an amateur can do to renew worn parts in the gear assembly.

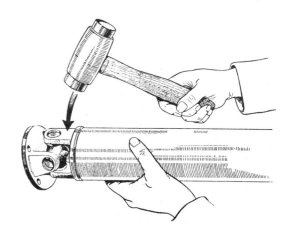

Fig 7:2 Extracting a bearing

Norman Frizzell Motor & General Ltd

Arrangements for your motor insurance having been completed, we have pleasure in enclosing the relevant documents.

It would be appreciated if you would check all items carefully and advise us at once of any omission or error.

Please quote the insurance number on all communications concerning this insurance.

ENCLOSURES

☒ Insurance document

☒ Schedule to Insurance document

☒ R.T.A. Certificate

☐ Membership document(s)

☐ Cheque value £ .
   (Premium overpayment)

Form 282P

Fig 7:3 A cut-away view of the rear axle

For example, fitting a new crown wheel and pinion involves four operations: (1) Setting the position of the pinion, (2) Adjusting the bearing pre-load, (3) Adjusting the differential bearing pre-load, (4) Adjusting the backlash between the gears. As numerous special tools and gauges are needed to carry out such accurate settings, the services of a competent agent are essential.

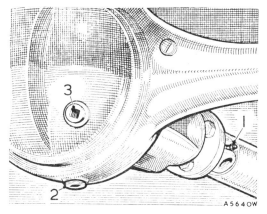

Fig 7:4 Location of rear universal joint nipple 1, drain plug 2 and filler-level plug 3 (later models)

Lubrication

Fig 7:4 shows the location of the filler and drain plugs. The filler plug is also a level indicator, and if no lubricant flows when the plug is removed, then fresh hypoid oil of the correct grade must be added. On early cars the filler plug will be found on the right-hand side of the gear carrier, see **FIG 7:5**.

Removing axle shafts

1 Jack up the appropriate side of the car and remove the wheel, chocking the others for safety.
2 Unscrew the brake drum locating screw, release the handbrake and tap off the drum. Now drain the rear axle.
3 Looking at **FIG 7:5**, remove screw 24 from the axle shaft flange and draw out the shaft. If tight, strike the shaft with a hide hammer until a gap shows between the flanges. Lever the shaft away with a screwdriver, renewing the paper joint washer on assembly if it is damaged.

Replacing shaft

1 Press and rotate the shaft until the splines enter. The paper joint must be about .010 in thick if it is hand-made. Anything thinner will inevitably lead to oil leaks.
2 The screw holding the axle shaft to the hub flange must be put in the countersunk hole so that it finishes up flush.
3 Finally restore the drake drum and fixing screw, re-adjust the shoes on both sides and replace the wheel.

Removing the hubs

1 After the axle shaft is withdrawn, knock back the keyed lock-washer 22 and remove it after unscrewing nut 23.
2 The hub is drawn off using an extractor bolted to the

wheel studs, the extractor screw pressing on a pad located on the axle casing end.

3 The bearing 21 and oil seal 20 can be drifted out. The bearing is not adjustable and must be renewed if worn. The oil seal is easily damaged and a tubular drift is needed when replacing it. It is an operation best left to an agent equipped with the special tool required. During reassembly, pack the hub with grease.

Note: FIG 7:6 shows the axle of later 'Sprites' and 'Midgets', from which it will be seen that the hub is fitted with an extra ring oil seal 42. The illustration also shows the axle shaft and hub for wire wheels, and the mounting bracket for the rear spring and link.

Rear springs—Austins A30, A35 and A40

On these cars the springs are semi-elliptic with silentbloc bushes in the spring eyes and shackles, except that on early cars the shackle bearing on the body is of bronze and needs periodical lubrication.

Maintenance

1 Examine the spring-to-axle 'U' bolts and tighten the nuts if necessary.
2 Wipe the damper filler plugs free from dirt, check the fluid level and top up if required.
3 Clean the springs and wipe with an oily rag.
4 Examine each spring leaf for breaks, and the bushes for wear.

Removing springs

1 Jack up the car on the side from which the spring is to be removed.
2 Take out the brake cable clevis pin.
3 Put blocks under the chassis rear cross member, as near to the rear anchorage of the spring as possible
4 Jack up the centre of the spring to relieve the tension.
5 Remove the wheel.
6 Unscrew the four self-locking nuts from the 'U' bolts holding the axle to the spring.
7 Unscrew the nut on the inside of the upper rear shackle, and the locknut and spring washer from the inside of the lower rear shackle.
8 Remove the inner shackle link and remove the outer link together with the two shackle pins.
9 At the front end of the spring, unscrew the inner nut and washer and drive the pin clear.
10 Upon removing the jack, the spring will come away.

Dismantling springs

1 Place the spring on its side and grip in a vice near the centre bolt.
2 Prise open the leaf clips, then unscrew the nut from the centre pin and drive out the pin.
3 Open the vice so that the spring leaves separate. Reverse the proceedings to reassemble.

Replacing

1 Ensure that the head of the spring centre bolt registers with the hole in the axle casing.
2 The rear upper shackle pin self-locking nut must not be fully tightened but the pin allowed freedom to move in its bronze bush.

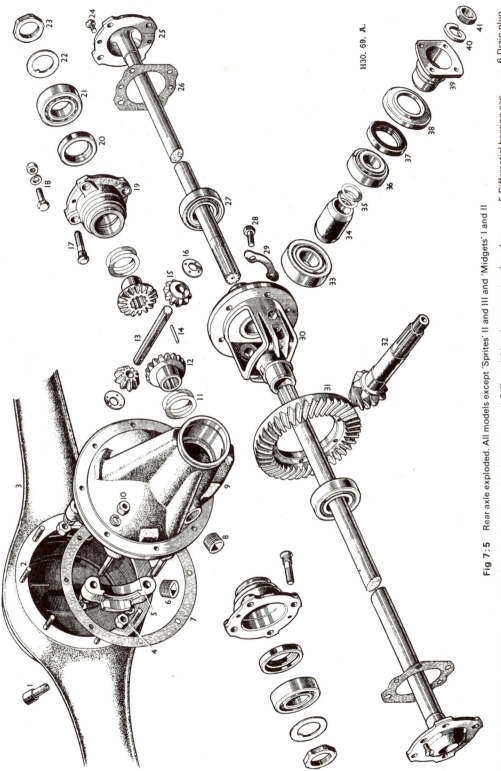

Fig 7:5 Rear axle exploded. All models except 'Sprites' II and III and 'Midgets' I and II

H30. 69. **A**.

Key to Fig 7:5 1 Axle breather.   2 Gear carrier stud.   3 Axle case.   4 Differential bearing cap nut and washer.   5 Differential bearing cap.   6 Drain plug.
7 Gear carrier joint washer.   8 Filler plug (earlier models).   9 Gear carrier.   10 Gear carrier nut and washer.   11 Differential bearing packing shims.   12 Differential wheel.
13 Differential pinion shaft.   14 Differential shaft dowel pin.   15 Differential pinion.   16 Pinion thrust washer.   17 Wheel stud.   18 Backplate bolt, nut and washer.
19 Hub casing.   20 Hub oil seal.   21 Hub bearing.   22 Hub lockwasher.   23 Hub securing nut.   24 Axle shaft screw.   25 Axle shaft.   26 Joint washer.
27 Differential bearing.   28 Crown wheel setscrew.   29 Lockwasher.   30 Differential cage.   31 Crown wheel.   32 Bevel pinion.   33 Bevel pinion rear bearing.
34 Pinion bearing distance piece.   35 Bevel pinion shims.   36 Bevel pinion front bearing.   37 Oil seal.   38 Oil seal housing.   39 Bevel pinion flange.
40 Bevel pinion spring washer.   41 Bevel pinion nut.

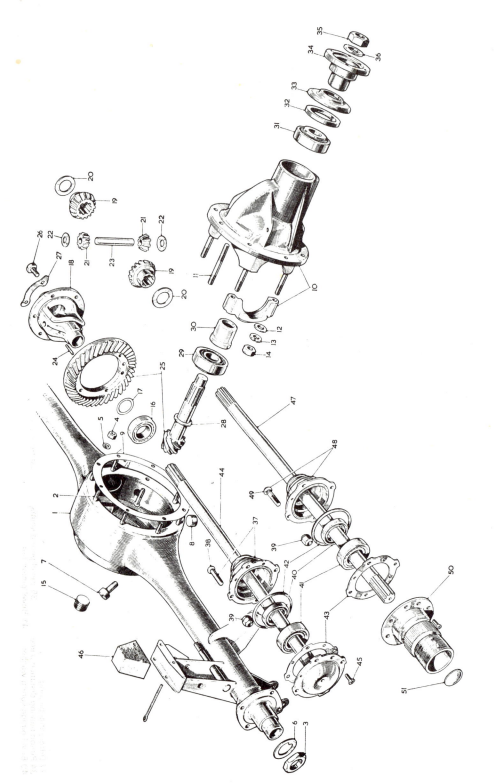

Fig 7:6 The axle of later 'Sprites' and 'Midgets'. Note hub and shaft for wire wheels.

Key to Fig 7:6   1 Case assembly.   2 Gear carrier stud.   3 Bearing retaining nut.   4 Gear carrier stud.   5 Spring washer.   6 Washer.   7 Breather assembly.
8 Drain plug.   9 Gear carrier joint.   10 Carrier assembly.   11 Bearing cap stud.   12 Plain washer.   13 Spring washer.   14 Nut.   15 Filler plug.
16 Differential bearing.   17 Bearing packing washer.   18 Differential cage.   19 Differential wheel.   20 Thrust washer.   21 Differential pinion.   22 Thrust washer.
23 Pinion ping.   24 Pinion peg.   25 Crown wheel and pinion.   26 Bolt.   27 Lock washer.   28 Pinion thrust washer.   29 Inner pinion bearing.   30 Bearing spacer.
31 Pinion outer bearing.   32 Oil seal.   33 Dust cover.   34 Universal joint flange.   35 Pinion nut.   36 Spring washer.   37 Hub assembly.   38 Wheel stud.
39 Nut.   40 Oil seal.   41 Hub bearing.   42 Oil seal ring.   43 Hub shaft joint.   44 Axle shaft.   45 Screw.   46 Bump rubber.   The following for
wire wheels only :   47 Axle shaft.   48 Hub assembly.   49 Wheel stud.   50 Hub extension.   51 Welch plug.

78

3 Do not tighten the other shackle pin nuts until the springs have been deflected under a normal working load. The bushes will then be subjected to equal torsion in each direction during service. Unequal loading leads to excessive torsion in one direction, causing rapid deterioration.

Removing axle—Austins A30, A35 and A40, Mk I

1 Chock the front wheels, release the hand brake and disconnect the brake cable at the balance lever.
2 Disconnect the propeller shaft at the rear end.
3 Detach the damper links where they are secured to the axle by nuts and spring washers.
4 Jack up the car on both sides. Remove the four 'U' bolt nuts under each spring retaining plate and tap the 'U' bolts clear. The axle can then be removed, looking out for the pad on top of the spring.

To refit the axle reverse these proceedings. The pad just mentioned fits over the head of the spring centre bolt which holds the leaves together. Locate this carefully so that the bolt head will enter the hole in the axle mounting bracket.

Removing axle—Austin A40, Mk II

Telescopic dampers are fitted to the later A40's making some difference to the method of removing and replacing the axle.

1 Block the wheels, release the hand brake, disconnect the brake cable at the balance lever and disconnect the hydraulic pipeline.
2 Disconnect the propeller shaft at the rear end and the nuts and washers 1 from the lower end of the dampers, see FIG 7:7.
3 Jack or block up the car under the frame and remove both wheels. Unscrew nuts 2, detaching the spring plate and the 'U' bolts.
4 Remove the axle sideways, taking care of the pad on top of the spring.

Reverse the order of dismantling when replacing the axle, being careful to fit the pad so that the centre pin of the spring fits up into the hole in the axle mounting bracket. Finally, reconnect the brake pipeline and bleed the brakes.

Removing axle—'Sprites' I and II, 'Midget' I

As these cars are fitted with quarter-elliptic springs there are some changes in procedure.

1 Raise the car by placing a jack under the differential casing. Place supports under the rear spring anchorages to the body.
2 Withdraw the exhaust down pipe, the silencer and the tail pipe.
3 Keeping the jack in position release the check strap where it is bolted to the body.
4 Release the damper arm from the connecting link.
5 Disconnect the upper suspension link from the rear axle bracket by unscrewing the nut and bolt.
6 Disconnect the handbrake cable at the cable adjustment, see the chapter on Brakes.
7 Disconnect the propeller shaft at the rear end.
8 Disconnect the hydraulic brake pipe at the main union just forward of the differential housing.
9 With the jack taking the full weight of the axle, unscrew and remove the shackle pins, then lower the axle and

withdraw from the car.

When replacing the axle, if it has been withdrawn from the car and the upper suspension link removed, do not tighten the shackle pins until the upper link is in position.

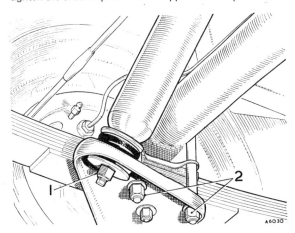

Fig 7:7   Rear telescopic damper mounting

Key to Fig 7:7   1 Damper nut.   2 Retaining plate nuts.

Removing springs—'Sprites' I and II, 'Midget' I

Follow the operations for removing the axle. Extract the two set bolts 1 at the front end of the spring as shown in FIG 7:8. Unscrew the 'U' bolt nuts 3, remove the 'U' bolt and the spring can then be pulled out of its mounting. Upon reassembly, tighten the shackle bolts after the normal working load has been applied to the springs.

Fig 7:8   Rear spring mounting on later 'Sprites' and 'Midgets'.

Key to Fig 7:8   1 Spring bolts.   2 Damper nuts.   3 'U' bolt nuts

Removing axle—'Sprite' III and 'Midget' II

The same axle is used, but suspension is by rubber-mounted semi-elliptic springs, with rubber bushes in the spring eyes and shackles.

Remove the axle as before, but take off the wheels and detach the check straps at the axle end. Release the axle by unscrewing the 'U' bolt nuts under the spring retaining plates. With all the weight of the axle on the jack, remove the rear shackle pins and the axle can then be lifted away. When replacing the axle follow earlier instructions about deflecting the springs before tightening the shackle bolts.

Removing springs—'Sprite' III and 'Midget' II

Raise the car, using a jack under the differential housing, and support the body. The weight of the axle must be taken by the jack and the springs must be fully unloaded. Remove the wheels. From inside the car, take out the set screws securing the front anchor bracket to the rear of the foot-well. Remove the other set screws in the bracket from under the car. Remove the four 'U' bolt nuts and damper anchorage plates from each spring. Remove the rear shackle nuts, pins and plates and lift out the spring assembly.

When refitting the 'U' bolts it will be helpful to remove the check strap.

Deflect the springs before tightening the shackle bolts.

Dampers—all cars except the Austin A40, Mk II

These are the Armstrong double-acting hydraulic type with access for topping up. The A40, Mk I has a stabilising bar attached to the damper arms.

Testing

There is no provision for adjustment, but it is possible to test the dampers by removing them and gripping the mounting lugs in a vice. Move the arm steadily up and down, when a moderate resistance should be felt throughout each stroke. If the resistance is erratic, with free movement of the arm noticeable, it may indicate lack of fluid. If there is no improvement after fluid has been added a new or replacement unit must be fitted. If the arm proves to be immoveable it is again a case of renewing the unit.

When dampers are removed from the car it is important to keep them as upright as possible to prevent trouble from aeration of the fluid.

Topping up

Use the recommended damper fluid for replenishment. If this is not available a good-quality mineral oil to Specification S.E.A. 20/20W is acceptable, although it is not suitable for low temperatures and is deficient in other ways. While adding fluid, work the arm through full strokes to expel air. Fill to the bottom of the filler plug hole.

Access to the filler plugs can be gained by removing the rear seat cushion and then the two rubber plugs near each wheel arch.

Refitting

The rubber bushes integral with both ends of the damper-to-axle connecting links cannot be renewed, so the whole link must be replaced.

On cars fitted with a stabilising bar, always fit the bar first and then attach the connecting links. Leave all connections loose until everything is in place and then tighten up.

Dampers—Austin A40, Mk II

These are telescopic as shown in **FIG 7:7**. They cannot be adjusted or topped up, so that defective dampers must be replaced by new ones.

Removing

Unscrew the nut and washer 1. Jack up the rear of the car under the frame on the side concerned. The damper spigot will then disengage from the spring retaining plate. After removing the top mounting nut and washer the damper can be detached. Testing should reveal the same kind of steady resistance found with the earlier type of damper.

Modifications

On 'Sprite' I the damper mounting brackets were modified. From car No. AN5/4333 intermittently to car No. 4507, and from No. 4508 onwards, modified dampers and body mounting brackets were fitted. The brackets, which previously supported only the forward ends of the upper suspension arms, were made to accommodate the damper fixing bolts. The dampers were positioned at a different angle to the horizontal and had shorter arms with longer connecting links. This involved changes to the connecting link attachment brackets welded to the axle casing, the new casing having Part No. ATA7419. The modified components are not interchangeable with the original type.

FAULT DIAGNOSIS

(a) Noisy axle

1 Insufficient or incorrect lubricant
2 Worn bearings
3 Worn gears

(b) Excessive backlash

1 Worn gears, bearings or bearing housings
2 Worn axle shaft splines
3 Worn universal joints
4 Loose or broken wheel studs. Worn wire wheel hub splines

(c) Oil leakage

1 Defective seals in hub
2 Defective pinion shaft seal
3 Defective seals on universal joint spiders

(d) Vibration

1 Propeller shaft out of balance
2 Worn universal joint bearings

(e) Rattles

1 Rubber bushes in damper links worn through
2 Dampers loose
3 Spring 'U' bolts loose
4 Loose spring clips
5 Worn bushes in spring eyes and shackles
6 Broken spring leaves

(f) 'Settling'

1 Weak or broken spring leaves
2 Badly worn spring bushes and shackle pins
3 Loose spring anchorages

CHAPTER 8

FRONT SUSPENSION

Operation   Lubrication   Servicing springs   Servicing suspension   Servicing hubs
Dampers   Stabilizer bar   Settings   Modifications   Fault diagnosis

Each front suspension unit consists of a pair of links which are pivoted at their inner ends. The outer ends are connected by a swivel pin carried on trunnion bearings, the pin passing through a swivel axle on which the brake and wheel are mounted. The lower link is a wide-based triangle to give stiffness against road shocks and braking stresses. The upper link is actually the arm of a double-acting hydraulic damper which is bolted to the car body. Between the lower link and a body abutment is a heavy-duty spring.

FIG 8:1 shows a unit exploded into its component parts. The lower link is carried on fulcrum pins 20 which pass through brackets on the body. The bearings are rubber bushes 21 and 23. The swivel pin 32 is cottered to fulcrum pin 27 and has a trunnion link 7 bolted to it at the top end. The trunnion is flexibly connected to the damper arm by pin 8 and rubber bushes 6. Turning on the swivel pin is the bushed swivel axle 36, partial rotation being imparted to it by steering arm 3. The stub of the swivel axle carries the brake mechanism and the road wheel. Spring seat 17 is bolted to the lower link and locates spring 16.

The following instructions will cover Austins, 'Sprites' and 'Midgets', as their suspension systems are practically identical. The only real differences are the use of rack-and-pinion steering on the sports cars and the introduction of disc brakes on the later 'Sprites' and 'Midgets'.

Lubrication

FIG 8:2 shows the three grease nipples which need regular attention. A fourth nipple on the steering tie-rod ball joint lies behind the suspension, but will be found in front with rack-and-pinion steering. There are two nipples on each swivel axle pin which are best lubricated when the weight of the car has been taken off the suspension by means of a jack. This allows grease to penetrate all round the bushes.

Checking for wear

To check for wear of the swivel pin and bushes, jack up the car until the front wheels are off the ground. Grip the tyre at the top and bottom and try to rock the wheel by pushing at the top and pulling at the bottom, then reverse the process. Any free movement indicates wear.

The pivot shaft in the damper is tested for wear by dismantling the suspension so that the arm can be moved freely.

The rubber fulcrum pin bushes slowly deteriorate and must be renewed if they show signs of softening or permit side movement.

The lower fulcrum pin runs in threaded bushes. Excessive play at this point may be due to a worn pin, which can be renewed. If the bushes are worn the whole lower link must be replaced as the bushes cannot be extracted.

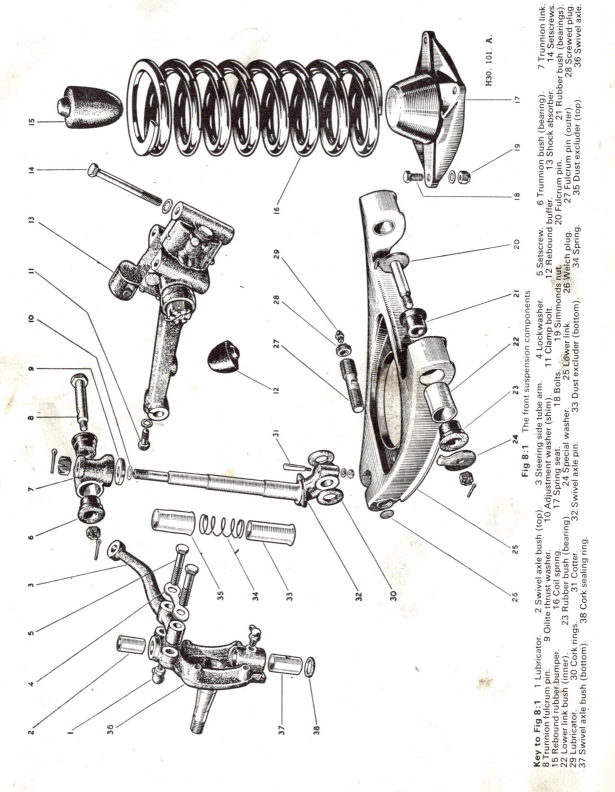

Fig 8:1   The front suspension components

H30. 101. A.

Key to Fig 8:1   1 Lubricator.   2 Swivel axle bush (top).   3 Steering side tube arm.   4 Lockwasher.   5 Setscrew.   6 Trunnion bush (bearing).   7 Trunnion link.
8 Trunnion fulcrum pin.   9 Oilite thrust washer.   10 Adjustment washer (shim).   11 Clamp bolt.   12 Rebound buffer.   13 Shock absorber.   14 Setscrews.
15 Rebound rubber-bumper.   16 Coil spring.   17 Spring seat.   18 Bolts.   19 Simmonds nut.   20 Fulcrum pin.   21 Rubber bush (bearings).
22 Lower link bush (inner).   23 Rubber bush (bearing).   24 Special washer.   25 Lower link.   26 Welch plug.   27 Fulcrum pin (outer).   28 Screwed plug.
29 Lubricator.   30 Cork rings.   31 Cotter.   32 Swivel axle pin.   33 Dust excluder (bottom).   34 Spring.   35 Dust excluder (top).   36 Swivel axle.
37 Swivel axle bush (bottom).   38 Cork sealing ring.

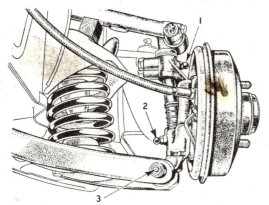

Fig 8:2   Lubrication points

Key to Fig 8:2   1 Swivel pin top bush.   **2** Swivel pin bottom bush.   **3** Lower link outer bushes.

Removing springs

1 Place a hard wood or metal block $1\frac{1}{8}$ in thick under the damper arm to keep it off the rubber rebound buffer when the car is jacked up.
2 Jack up the car on the side concerned.
3 Prepare two high-tensile bolts $4\frac{1}{2}$ in long, threaded all the way. Take out two diametrically opposite bolts from the spring seat and replace them with the slave bolts, which must be screwed up tight as in **FIG 8:3**. Remove the two remaining bolts and slacken off the nuts on the slave bolts until the spring is fully expanded and capable of being removed.

Reverse these operations to refit the spring if it is found to be without cracks and conforms with the dimensions given in Technical Data. Shortening is a sign of weakness.

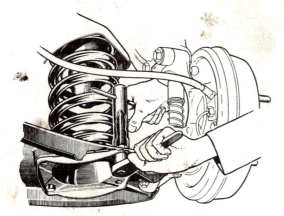

Fig 8:3   Using a pair of slave bolts to remove or replace a spring

Removing suspension

1 Jack up the car and remove the wheel and coil spring, as already explained.
2 Disconnect the steering side rod from the arm 3 in **FIG 8:1**. Note that this arm faces the opposite way on the 'Sprites' and 'Midgets'. If the tapered shank of the ball

pin is tight in the steering arm, slacken the nut a turn or two and tap the eye of the arm smartly on the side with a hammer, holding up on the other side with another hammer or a block of steel. This should jar the pin loose.
3 Disconnect the flexible brake hose at the inner end.
4 Remove the split pins and nuts from the fulcrum pins 20 at the inner end of the lower link. Take away the pin and the outer pair of rubber bushes 23, thus freeing the lower part of the suspension.
5 At the upper end, remove the clamp bolt 11 and shake-proof washer from the damper arm. Take off the split pin and nut on the fulcrum pin 8, tap the pin out and withdraw the rubber bushes 6. The suspension unit will now be free.

It is assumed that the brake drum and front hub have already been removed. Instructions for this operation are given in a later section. Now proceed to dismantle the suspension as follows.

Dismantling

1 Remove the brake back plate from the swivel axle 36. Release the steering lever 3 by knocking back the lock washer 4 and removing the bolts 5.
2 Remove the nut and split pin from the top of the axle pin 32. Take off the trunnion 7 and thrust washer 9. The shims 10 should be put in a safe place ready for reassembly.
3 Lift off the swivel axle 36 together with the dust excluder tubes 33 and 35, and their spring 34. At the bottom there is a cork sealing ring 38.
4 Slacken the nut on cotter pin 31 and tap the cotter loose. Remove the nut, spring washer and cotter.
5 Unscrew the lower fulcrum pin plug 28 and the pin 27. Swivel pin 32 will then come away with the cork sealing rings 30. If necessary, knock out the welch plug 26.

Examination

1 Using a micrometer, check the swivel pin for wear. The bushes 2 and 37 are also subject to wear. The bushes can be renewed, but they will then need individual broaching, which is an operation best done by someone with the necessary Service tools as the bushes must be kept in perfect alignment.
2 Test the fit of the fulcrum pin 27 in the lower link threaded bushes. If a worn pin is replaced by a new one and end play is still apparent, then the bushes are worn and the whole of the lower link assembly must be replaced as the bushes cannot be renewed separately. The larger bushes 22 are renewable and can be fitted and brazed into position.
3 Examine the damper for leaks, particularly round the cross-shaft bearings. If the shaft can be moved up and down or to the side, it is worn and the complete damper will need renewal. Remove it by unscrewing bolts 14. Check the damping effect by moving the arm up and down steadily through full strokes. Resistance should be even in both directions. Erratic movement could mean that the fluid level is low. Try topping up with correct damper fluid to just below the filler plug opening, moving the arm through several strokes to expel air. If there is then no improvement the damper must be replaced as it is not adjustable.

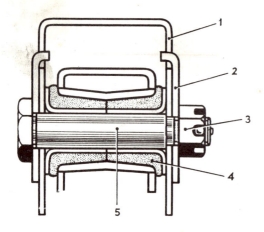

Fig 8:4 Inner end mounting of lower link

Key to Fig 8:4 1 Mounting bracket. 2 Special washer. 3 Castellated nut. 4 Rubber bush (bearing). 5 Fulcrum pin.

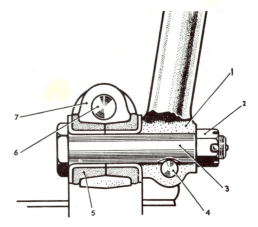

Fig 8:5 Trunnion link to damper arm assembly

Key to Fig 8:5 1 Damper arm. 2 Castellated nut. 3 Fulcrum pin. 4 Clamp bolt. 5 Rubber bush (bearing). 6 Swivel axle pin. 7 Trunnion link.

Reassembling suspension

The sectioned illustrations in **FIGS 8:4** and **8:5** show the lower and upper link mountings respectively. The correct assembly of the rubber bushes and fulcrum pins is clearly shown.

1 If any of the parts are new, check that the fulcrum pin is not tight in the threaded bushes nor in the lower trunnion of the swivel pin.

2 Position the cork rings 30 in the lower link, protecting their inner faces with very thin metal discs. Slide the swivel pin 32 into place with the cotter hole inside. The metal discs will prevent damage from the sharp edges of the swivel pin bosses. When the pin is located, draw out the discs with a pair of thin-nosed pliers.

3 Screw the fulcrum pin 27 into place in the lower link, the small end entering the larger threaded bush first. Line up the cotter pin slot with the hole in the swivel pin and tap the cotter home. If it proves difficult then check the alignment of the slot and hole. Secure the cotter.

4 Replace the threaded plug and nipple 28 and 29. Fit a new welch plug in the other end if the old one was removed. Treat the edges with jointing compound, fit with convex side outwards and flatten the dome with a large punch until the plug is firm and no more. Test for tightness by pumping oil through the grease nipple.

5 Slip a new cork sealing ring 38 over the swivel pin with the chamfered side downwards, then smear the pin with oil.

6 Fit the dust excluders 33 and 34 and the spring 35 in the order shown.

7 Screw the two grease nipples into the swivel axle 36 so that they will face to the rear. Slide the axle over the pin and check for full lock in both directions.

8 Replace the thrust washer 9 and the shim 10 followed by the trunnion 7 with its cross-bore outwards. Re-

place and tighten the castellated nut. When the axle is moved from lock to lock there should be slight resistance with no sign of vertical slackness. This condition is reached by putting on or taking off shims 10. These are available in thicknesses of .008 in and .012 in.

9 Fit the brake back-plate assembly with the flexible hose to the front and the bleed nipple pointing upwards at the rear. Fit the hub and brake drum either now or after the suspension unit is back on the car.

Replacing

1 If new rebound bumpers are to be fitted, wet the spring bumper and push it into the hole in the bottom of the damper mounting plate and the damper arm buffer 12 in the top.

2 Wet two of the large rubber bearings 21 and put one inside each lower link boss. Lift the link into position on the car and insert the pins 20 from the inside so that the tab registers. Replace the outer pair of rubber bushes 23, then the special washer 24 followed by the castellated nut, which is split-pinned when tight. See Note at the end about Nyloc nuts.

3 With the dismantling block still under the damper arm, connect the top end. Insert the two small rubber bearings 6 in the trunnion eye 7. Tap the fulcrum pin 8 from the rear so that it goes through both bearings and the damper arm, being careful to keep the clamp bolt notch at the top. Tighten the castellated nut on the fulcrum pin until the notch is in line with the clamp bolt hole in the damper arm, then split-pin the nut. Now tighten the clamp bolt on a shake-proof washer.

4 Replace the coil spring and road wheel. Lower the car off the jack so that the packing block can be removed from under the damper arm. Connect the flexible hose and bleed the brakes.

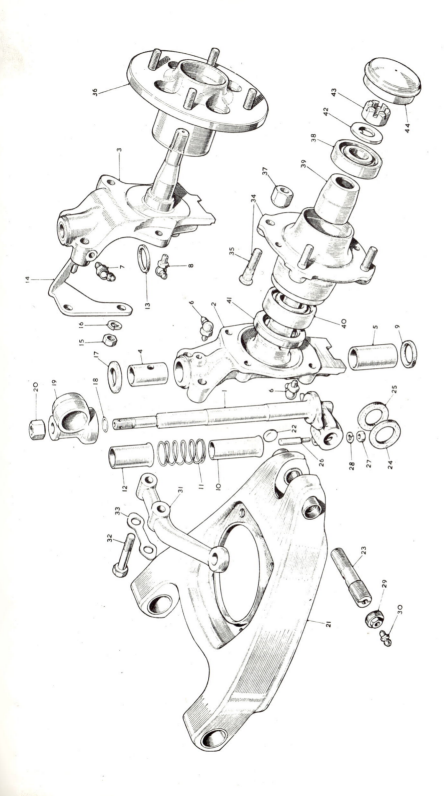

Fig 8:6   Front suspension components for 'Sprites' II and III and 'Midgets' I and II

Key to Fig 8:6   1 Swivel pin.   2 Swivel axle assembly.   3 Swivel axle assembly.   4 Bush (top).   5 Bush (bottom).   6 Lubricator.   7 Lubricator.   8 Lubricator.
9 Sealing ring.   10 Dust excluder tube (bottom).   11 Dust excluder spring.   12 Dust excluder tube (top).   13 Sealing ring.   14 Brake hose lock plate.   15 Nut.
16 Spring washer.   17 Thrust washer.   18 Adjustment washer.   19 Suspension trunnion link.   20 Nut.   21 Lower link.   22 Plug.   23 Fulcrum pin.
24 Ring (large).   25 Ring (small).   26 Cotter pin.   27 Nut.   28 Spring washer.   29 Screwed plug.   30 Lubricator.   31 Steering lever.   32 Set screw.
33 Lock washer.   34 Hub assembly.   35 Wheel stud.   36 Hub assembly.   37 Nut.   38 Outer hub bearing.   39 Bearing distance piece.   40 Inner hub bearing.
41 Oil seal.   42 Retaining washer.   43 Nut.   44 Cap.

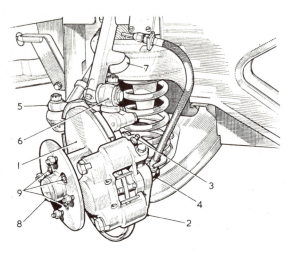

Fig 8:7   Front suspension with disc brake

Key to Fig 8:7   1 Brake disc.   2 Calliper assembly.
3 Bleeder screw.   4 Calliper fluid connector.   5 Steering
lever.   6 Suspension trunnion link.   7 Rebound buffer.
8 Retaining cap.   9 Brake disc to hub securing bolts.

Suspension—'Sprites' II and III, and 'Midgets' I and II

Owners of these cars will notice in **FIG 8:6** that the steering arm is shown facing forwards in the correct position. Otherwise the component parts are the same as those already described with the exception of the swivel axle 3 in the top right-hand corner. This, and the associated components, is used for disc brakes. **FIG 8:7** also shows the disc brake. Details for removing the hub will be given in the next section.

Hubs

The front hub bearings are not adjustable and slackness may indicate wear and the need for replacements. Check by jacking up the car until the wheel concerned is clear of the ground. Remove the wheel and hub caps. Grasp the wheel horizontally and try to rock it. Any movement between the hub and the swivel axle nut shows that the bearings are worn.

Dismantling

The hub assembly for drum brakes is shown in **FIG 8:8**. Refer to this when using the following instructions.
1 Jack up the car, remove the wheel and brake drum.
2 Take out split pin 3 and unscrew nut 2. Use an extractor to pull off the hub.
3 Knock out each bearing by using a drift inserted in the opposite end. The oil seal 9 will precede the inner bearing 8.

If the bearings feel rough and there is noticeable slackness between the inner and outer races they must be renewed. Also renew the oil seal if leakage at the inner end has been troublesome.

Assembling

1 Press the outer bearing into the hub with the face marked 'thrust' entering first.
2 Turn the hub over, pack it with the recommended

grease, and place the distance piece 6 in position with the reduced end towards the outer bearing. This distance piece is accurately made to such a length that the bearings are pre-loaded when the axle nut is tight. Do not interfere with the piece nor use packing.
3 Press the inner bearing into place, again with the face marked 'thrust' towards the distance piece. Replace the oil seal 9 with its lipped end towards the inner bearing as can be seen in the illustration.
4 Replace the hub on the swivel axle, using a tubular drift which spans the face of the outer bearing so that the pressure is evenly distributed. A piece of thin-walled tubing over the axle threads will protect them from damage during this operation.
5 Replace washer 4 with the peg located in the axle slot and screw on nut 2.
6 Put on the brake drum and tighten the screw in the countersunk hole. Tighten a pair of wheel nuts on diametrically opposite studs and check that the drum revolves freely.
7 Tighten the castellated nut 2 to the torque wrench reading given in Technical Data. Insert the split pin to lock the nut.
8 Wipe grease round the face of the outer bearing, do not put any in the hub cap 1 and replace the cap.
9 Fit the wheel and wheel nuts, lower the car and then tighten the nuts fully. Replace the wheel cap.

Disc brake hubs

To remove these, after taking off the road wheel, disconnect the brake calliper assembly as detailed in the chapter on Brakes. Support the assembly, as it must not be allowed to hang on the hydraulic hose. Pull off the hub and disc assembly. The hub and disc are parted by unscrewing bolts 9 in **FIG 8:7**. Dismantle the hub, following the instructions for the drum brake hub. When refitting, check the run-out of the disc at the outer edge. It must not exceed .006 in and adjustment can be made by trying the disc in another position on the hub. All the details given for refitting drum brake hubs are correct for disc brakes.

Dampers

These are hydraulic double-acting types and the instructions given for servicing the same type of damper used on the rear suspension can be followed.

Removing

1 Jack up the car and put blocks under the body in safe positions. Remove the road wheel and place a jack under the outer end of the lower link arm, raising it until the damper arm is clear of the rebound buffer.
2 Remove the damper arm clamp bolt and the castellated nut on the fulcrum pin. Withdraw the pin and the rubber bushes in the trunnion link.
3 Unscrew the three long bolts holding the damper body to the car.

Note: The jack must be left in place under the lower link while the top arm remains disconnected so that the coil spring is kept securely in position, and no strain is put on the steering connections.

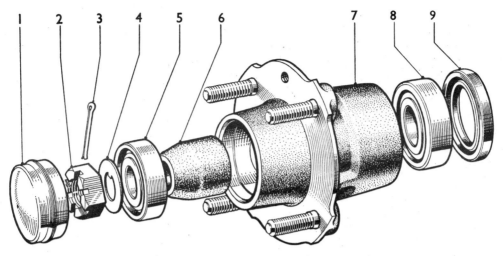

Fig 8:8   Front hub assembly

Key to Fig 8:8   1 Hub cap.   2 Castellated nut.   3 Split pin.   4 Locating washer.   5 Outer bearing.   6 Distance piece.
7 Hub.   8 Inner bearing.   9 Oil seal.

Reassembly

Reverse the dismantling procedure but attend to the following points.

1   Do not tighten the damper mounting bolts beyond a torque wrench loading of 30 lb/ft as over-tightening may affect the performance of the damper.

2   Before fitting the upper fulcrum pin, work the damper arm three or four times through its full travel to expel any air. At all times keep the damper as near as possible to its normal working position to avoid such aeration.

3   Renew the rubber bushes in the trunnion link if they have softened and allow excessive side movement.

Stabilizer bar

This is fitted to the A40 Mk II, and the mounting to the lower link is shown in **FIG 8:9**. The bar itself turns in bushes held in brackets attached to the body side-members. All the earlier instructions for removing and replacing the suspension system are correct, but the bar must be removed first. To do this remove the nuts and washers securing each end of the bar to the lower links. Remove the four bolts and washers holding the brackets to the side-members and lift the bar away. Refit the bar last in every case.

Settings

There are three angles in the front suspension geometry which have an important effect upon the steering and riding qualities of the car. If the suspension has been damaged these angles cannot be restored by adjustment. They must be checked against the manufacturer's figures to see whether new parts are needed. The correct angles are given in Technical Data.

FIG 8:10 should be studied to understand the three angles.

Castor angle

This is shown at A and is the tilt of the swivel pin when viewed from the side of the car. This could be affected by damage to the upper and lower links.

Swivel pin inclination

The centre illustration at B shows the tilt of the swivel pin when viewed from the front of the car. This too is most likely to be affected by damage to the links. Check with an alignment gauge.

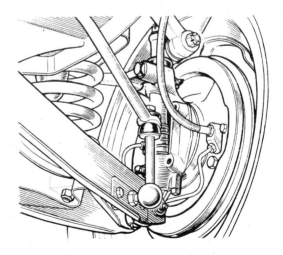

Fig 8:9   The stabilizer bar mounting on A40 11

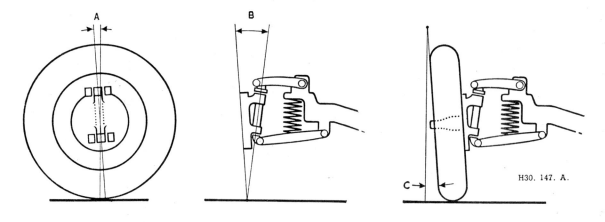

Fig 8:10 Front suspension settings. A castor angle, B swivel pin inclination and C camber angle

Camber angle

This is the outward tilt of the wheel as shown at C. It can be roughly checked in the following way. Put the un-laden car on a piece of level ground and ensure that the tyres are uniform and have the same pressure. Hang a plumb line from the outside wall of the tyre vertically above the hub. Measure the distance from the line to the outside wall of the tyre vertically below the hub. This distance must be the same for both wheels. Damage to the links and general wear will affect this angle.

Modifications

On later chassis the lower link inner fulcrum pins are secured by Nyloc self-locking nuts. These replace the castellated nuts and split pins formerly used. If the Nyloc nuts are removed at any time, NEW nuts must be used on reassembly.

FAULT DIAGNOSIS

(a) Wheel wobble

1 Unbalanced wheels and tyres
2 Slack steering connections
3 Incorrect steering angles
4 Excessive play in steering gear

5 Broken or weak front springs
6 Worn hub bearings

(b) Wander

1 Check 2, 3 and 4 in (a)
2 Front suspension and rear axle mounting points out of alignment
3 Uneven tyre pressures
4 Uneven tyre wear
5 Weak dampers or springs

(c) Heavy steering

1 Check 3 in (a)
2 Very low tyre pressures
3 Insufficient lubricant in steering rack
4 Unlubricated steering connections
5 Wheels out of track
6 Incorrectly adjusted steering gear
7 Misaligned steering column

(d) Tyre squeal

1 Check 3 in (a) and 2 in (c)

CHAPTER 9

STEERING

Operation   *Cam and Peg*   *Worm and Nut*   *Toe-in*   *End play*   *Dismantling*
Servicing   *Idler*   *Ball joint connections*   *Rack and Pinion*   *Toe-in*   *Backlash*
End play   *Ball joints*   *Dismantling*   *Servicing*   *Fault diagnosis*

Three kinds of steering gearbox will be covered by this chapter, the cam-and-peg type as fitted to the A30, A35 and A40, the worm and nut type fitted to the A30 and A35 as an alternative, and the rack and pinion type fitted to the 'Sprites' and 'Midgets'.

There is no difference in the steering layout of the cam and peg, or the worm and nut types, and **FIG 9:1** shows it as viewed from the front of the car. From this it can be seen that sideways movement of lever 4 is transmitted to the side rod 2. This in turn moves the steering arm of the right-hand road wheel. The same motion is also passed by cross-tube 3 to lever 5 and so to the other side rod 2. This will then turn the left-hand wheel through the second steering arm.

Lever 4 is splined to the rocker shaft in the steering gearbox, the shaft being number 4 in **FIG 9:2.** This illustration shows the component parts of the cam and peg gearbox, and the numbers are used in the following description. Peg 3 on the arm of the rocker shaft 4 engages in the spiral groove of cam 20. The cam is attached to the steering column, and rotation of the cam will cause the arm of the rocker shaft to move in an arc. This motion is repeated by lever 23 which is splined to the shaft at its lower end.

A similar action is produced by the worm and nut gearbox featured in **FIG 9:3.** Rotation of worm 21 causes nut 22 to slide to and fro. Peg 6 fits into a slot in the top of the nut and consequently travels in an arc as the nut slides.

The following instructions apply to the cam and peg and to the worm and nut types of steering gear. The rack and pinion type will be covered later.

Maintenance

Accurate steering can be maintained only by regular lubrication. There are six grease nipples on the side rods and the cross tube, as shown in **FIG 9:1,** unless the ball joints are found to be without nipples in which case they are self-lubricating. There are four nipples for the swivel axle bushes and two on the lower link fulcrum pins. These can be located by reference to the previous chapter on the front suspension.

Using the specified grades of oil, top up the steering gearbox and the idler to the level of the filler plug openings.

Toe-in

The correct figure for toe-in is given in Technical Data. Adjustment to toe-in is made by turning cross tube 3 in **FIG 9:1,** after releasing the locknuts at each end.

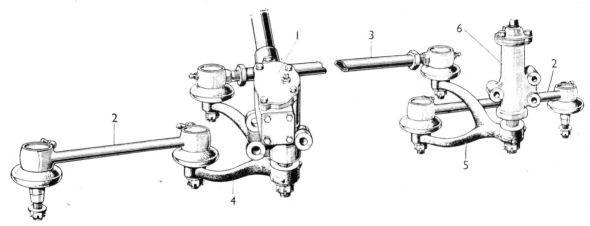

Fig 9:1   The steering layout of A30's, 35's and 40's

Key to Fig 9:1   1 Steering box.   2 Side tubes.   3 Cross tube.   4 Steering side and cross-tube lever.
5 Steering side and cross-tube lever.   6 Steering idler.

1 Bring the car to rest after a forward movement so that
   the wheels are in the normal running position. Have the
   tyres inflated equally.
2 Measure the distance between the tyres or the rims at
   wheel centre height at the front. Mark the points of
   measurement and roll the car forward for exactly half a
   revolution so that the marks are at the rear.
      Measure again between these points. The difference
   between the measurements is the amount of toe-in or
   toe-out.

End play—cam and peg

   FIG 9:2 shows the cam 20 and its bearings 16 with
shims 17 for adjusting end play in the column. Proceed as
follows.

1 Disconnect the side rod and cross tube from lever 23.
2 Turn the steering partly to the right or left lock and have
   a second operator to hold the steering wheel rim without exerting end pressure on the column.
3 Try to move the lever 23 from side to side. If there is end
   play the steering wheel will be seen to move up and
   down.
4 Remove the end cover 18, having a tray handy to catch
   the oil draining from the box.
5 Add or remove shims until there is no play but the
   steering wheel will nevertheless move freely when held
   lightly at the rim with the thumb and forefinger. On
   assembly refill the gearbox with oil.

End play—worm and nut

   FIG 9:3 shows the steering column bearing assembly
in the top right-hand corner. The parts 10, 11, 12 and 13
are fitted over the top end of the column in the order
shown. To take up end play, follow the sequence 1, 2 and
3 in the previous section, then:

1 Slacken the locknut and turn the adjustable cup 11 until
   there is no float and yet the steering wheel is quite free.
   Tightening the locknut while holding the cup 11 with
   a second spanner may have a tendency to tighten the
   bearing unduly and it is advisable to slacken the cup
   back a little to allow for this.

   In each case do not forget to reconnect the side rod and
cross tube.

Adjusting rocker shaft

   This adjustment is done in the same way on both types
of steering gearbox, the cam and peg, and the worm and
nut.

1 With the side rod and cross tube still disconnected,
   slacken the adjusting screw locknut 9 in **FIG 9:2** and
   2 in **FIG 9:3**. Turn the screw in to take up backlash.
2 Check the adjustment in the straight ahead position.
   The reason for this is that the cam or the worm was
   designed so that a slight amount of backlash would be
   present on either lock. This compensated for the extra
   wear on the parts in the straight ahead position. The
   adjustment is correct when a 'tight' spot is barely
   apparent when the steering wheel is moved past the
   centre position.
3 Reconnect the side rod and cross tube.

REMOVING STEERING GEAR

On the A30 and A35

1 Prise out the emblem cap from the steering wheel hub,
   unscrew the wheel securing nut and draw the wheel
   off the column. On later models a retaining ring, instead
   of a machined shoulder, is inserted and pinned into a
   corresponding recess in the wheel.
2 Remove the road wheel on the steering side, and take
   out the distributor.
3 Detach the side rod and cross tube from the steering
   lever, release the nut securing the lever and draw it off
   its splines.
3 From inside the car remove the two screws which hold
   the lighting switch strap to the column. Also withdraw the strap which fastens the column beneath the
   glove box.
4 From inside the bonnet take out the three set screws
   which hold the steering box bracket to the body. Withdraw the column and box complete through the bonnet
   opening.

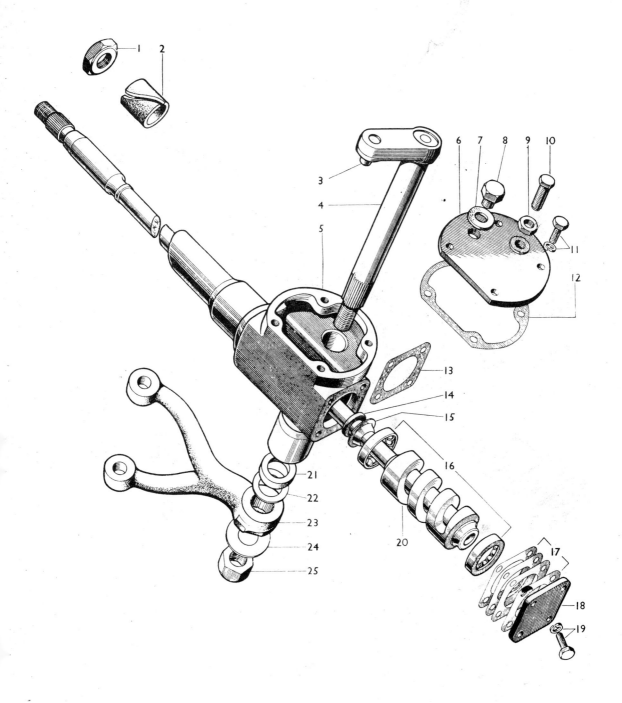

Fig 9:2   Components of the cam and peg steering unit

Key to Fig 9:2

1 Steering wheel securing nut.   2 Felt bush for inner column.   3 Peg for rocker shaft.   4 Rocker shaft.   5 Housing for gear.
6 Side cover.   7 Washer for oil filler plug.   8 Oil filler plug.   9 Thrust screw locknut.   10 Thrust screw.
11 Cover setscrew and washer.   12 Side cover joint washer.   13 End cover joint washer.   14 Rubber ring for top bearing
retaining cup (for assembly only).   15 Top bearing retaining cup (for assembly only).   16 Bearing ball cups and balls.
17 Shims for adjustment.   18 End cover.   19 Setscrew and washer.   20 Cam and inner column.   21 Cork sealing washer.
22 Retaining disc.   23 Steering side and cross-tube lever.   24 Plain washer.   25 Nut.
Note: Item 25 replaced by a castellated nut and split pin on later chassis.

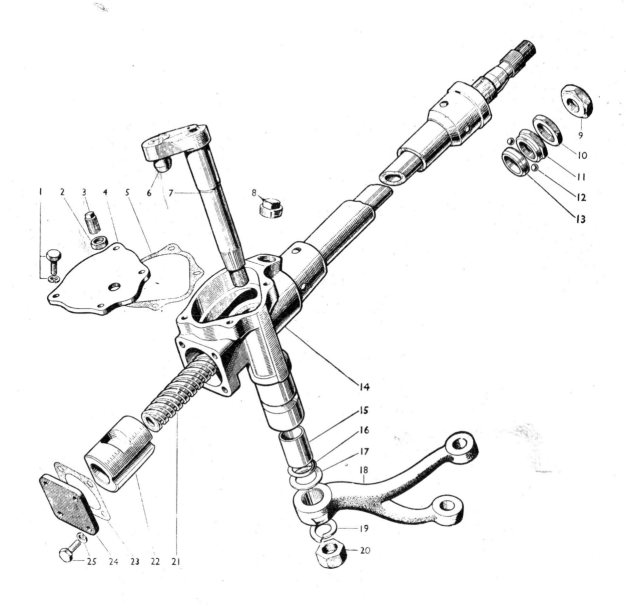

Fig 9:3   Components of the worm and nut steering unit

Key to Fig 9:3   1 Setscrew and washer for top cover.   2 Locknut.   3 Thrust screw.   4 Top cover.   5 Joint washer.
6 Rocker shaft peg.   7 Rocker shaft.   8 Oil filler plug.   9 Steering wheel securing nut.   10 Adjustable cup locknut.
11 Adjustable cup.   12 Balls for top bearing.   13 Fixed ball cup.   14 Steering box and outer column.   15 Bush for rocker shaft.
16 Oil seal.   17 Washer for oil seal.   18 Side and cross-tube lever.   19 Washer.   20 Nut or castellated nut and split pin.
21 Inner column and worm.   22 Worm nut.   23 End cover joint washer.   24 End cover.   25 End cover setscrew and washer.
Note: The worm nut 22 has not been shown in its correct position for assembly. The internally-threaded end should be towards the
filler plug, and the groove which runs the length of the nut must be away from the rocker shaft.

On the A40

1 Remove the parcel tray, and the battery.
2 Spring out the horn push and remove the steering wheel nut. Pull off the wheel with an extractor.
3 Remove the two screws from the column support bracket.
4 Disconnect the snap connectors to the light switch bracket. Take out the four screws holding the switch housing to the column and remove the switch.
5 Release the side rod and cross tube from the steering lever.
6 Take out the three set screws from the steering box mounting flange.
7 Pull out the column and box through the bonnet opening, turning the column so that the steering lever is upwards to clear the radiator.
8 When refitting simply reverse the process.

Dismantling—cam and peg

Looking at **FIG 9:2**, do the following:
1 Remove the cover plate 6.
2 Turn the box over and support the face so that the rocker shaft 4 can be driven out with a soft metal drift. Do not remove the peg 3 unless it is badly worn, as it is a drive fit.
3 Release the end cover 18, removing the shims 17 and joint washer 13. Take out the lower ball cup and the balls 16. Turn the column vertically with the box uppermost and bump the column on a block of wood. The inner column can then be drawn out, taking care to retrieve the balls from the upper cup 16.
4 Using a strong wire hook, pull out the felt bush 2 from the top of the column. Examine the parts for wear and renew them if necessary. The top felt bush 2 is fitted by smearing the new one with heavy oil and pushing it into place. To renew the oil seal 21, use a scraper to remove the metal which has been 'peened' over the retaining disc 22, prise it out, renew the parts and 'peen' over again.

Reassembling—cam and peg

Reverse the dismantling procedure, using the shims 17 to adjust the end play in the column. This must turn freely after the adjustment, as the bearings will be damaged by excessive pressure. Turn back adjusting screw 10 before refitting the cover plate 6, carrying out the final adjustment of the rocker shaft according to the instructions in an earlier section.

There is a clamping bolt in the steering box mounting bracket which must not be overtightened as it may lead to stiffness and possible seizure of the rocker shaft. Use a torque wrench reading of 23 to 25 lb/ft.

Dismantling—worm and nut

Using **FIG 9:3** as a guide follow this sequence.
1 Remove the top cover 4 and tap out the rocker shaft 7 as in the cam and peg instructions.
2 Remove the end cover 24 and joint washer 23.
3 At the top, unscrew the locknut 10 and the adjustable cup 11, collecting the loose balls.
4 Bump the top end of the inner column on a block of wood to withdraw it, together with the nut 22. Retrieve the fixed ball cup 13.

Reassembling—worm and nut

After replacing worn parts as detailed in the cam and peg instructions, reassemble the column first and adjust the top bearing so that there is no end play, yet without pre-loading the bearing. Complete the assembly in the same way as for the cam and peg type.

Steering idler

A glance at **FIG 9:1** will show the idler as part 6. This has been fitted in two forms, the early type being illustrated in **FIG 9:4** and the later in **FIG 9:5**.

Removing

1 Disconnect the side rod and cross tube from the idler lever.
2 Unscrew the three set screws holding the idler body to its mounting bracket and lift the idler and lever clear. Draw off the lever.

Dismantling—early type

1 Remove rubber cap 2.
2 Unscrew the idler shaft 3 by turning in a left-hand direction.
Replace worn parts. The oil seal 5 can be renewed by removing the burr which has been 'peened' over the retaining washer 6, and then prising out the washer. Insert a new seal followed by the washer and 'peen' over again to lock in place.

Assembling—early type

1 Screw the idler shaft right home after smearing with oil.
2 Fill oil reservoir 7 and replace cap 2.
Replace the idler in the car.

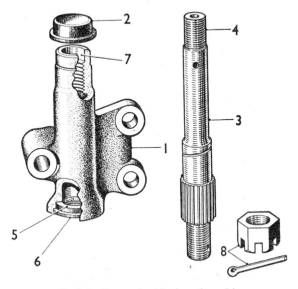

Fig 9:4 The steering idler for early models

Key to Fig 9:4 1 Idler body. 2 Rubber cap. 3 Idler shaft. 4 Retaining thread. 5 Oil seal. 6 Retaining washer. 7 Oil reservoir. 8 Castellated nut and split pin.

Note: Having fitted the complete idler it is important to turn the shaft 3 back by two complete turns from the uppermost position as assembled. This allows the shaft to turn freely on both locks without binding.

Dismantling—later type

1 Remove top cover 2, noting that the joint washers 6 are also an adjustment for end float of the shaft.
2 Draw the lever off the splines at the lower end of the shaft 3 and withdraw the shaft.

If there has been leakage from the oil seal at the lower end of the body, replace it by following the instructions given for the early type of idler.

Assembling—later type

1 Oil the shaft and replace in the body.
2 Fit the cover 2 and the joint washers 6, checking the end float of the shaft after screws 7 have been fully tightened. Adjust by adding or removing joint washers until the shaft will turn freely without end float.
3 Fill with oil to the level of the filler plug opening. Replace in the car.

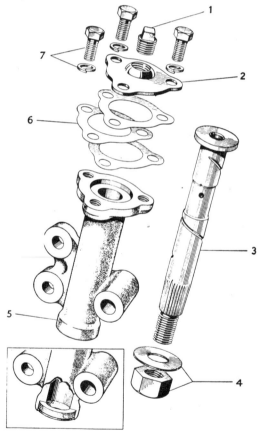

Fig 9:5 The steering idler for later models. Inset shows oil seal and retaining washer. Item 4 was replaced by a slotted nut and split pin

Key to Fig 9:5 1 Idler filler plug. 2 Cover. 3 Idler shaft. 4 Nut and washer. 5 Idler body. 6 Joint washer. 7 Set-screw and washer for cover.

Note: The plain nut 4 has been replaced by a castellated nut and split pin. The later type of idler is interchangeable with the early type as an assembly. The component parts are not interchangeable.

Steering connections

There are three types of ball end connections which have been fitted, the latest being a nylon type which is sealed for life and needs no lubrication. On this one, should a rubber boot become damaged in service, both boot and joint must be renewed. If, however, the boot is damaged during dismantling and the joint remains quite clean, a new boot only is required. Before fitting it, smear the area adjacent to the joint with Dextagrease Super GP. The other two joints are illustrated in **FIG 9:6.**

Early Austin type

This is shown by the central and left-hand sections in **FIG 9:6.** It can be seen that the lower ball socket is threaded for adjustment. Locking the socket is done by a split pin in castellations and split pin holes, the latter being drilled at a different pitch to the castellations so that fine adjustment is possible. To make an adjustment remove the split pin and tighten the socket. Then turn it back until the ball just moves freely with a castellation and a split pin hole in line. Insert the pin and replace the rubber boot snugly in its groove. Remember that accurate adjustment will be quite impossible if the ball pin is worn, in which case it must be replaced.

Later type

This is the Lockheed joint shown on the right in **FIG 9:6.** It is self-adjusting and needs no other attention than regular lubrication.

The ball pins of all types have tapered shanks fitting into the various steering levers. To remove them, slacken the castellated nut a turn or two and tap the boss of the lever on the side, with a smart hammer blow, holding up on the other side with another hammer or a block of steel. This will jar the taper loose.

When replacing the joints in the cross tube, ensure that they are in line with each other horizontally before tightening the locking nuts.

Rack and pinion steering

This is the type fitted to all the 'Sprites' and 'Midgets' and **FIG 9:7** shows it in exploded form. The illustration is of the later 'Sprite' and 'Midget' assembly but is basically correct for 'Sprite' I.

The rack housing 1 is secured to brackets above the front frame cross-member immediately behind the radiator. The housing contains the sliding rack 2. Each end of the rack carries a ball-jointed tie-rod 19 which is connected to the steering arm by ball joint 24. The inner steering column 51 is clamped to the splined end of the pinion 11, and this pinion engages the rack.

Maintenance

The lubricating nipple will be found on the left-hand side of the rack housing where it can be reached with the bonnet open. Give no more than ten strokes of a gun filled with hypoid oil at the specified intervals. Avoid overfilling the housing and keep the clips on the rubber gaiters 32 fully tightened to prevent loss of oil. It will also be necessary to lubricate the outer ball joints 24 if they are fitted with a nipple 36.

Toe-in

The correct figure for toe-in is given in Technical Data. Adjustment is made by altering the length of the tie-rods 19.

1 Inflate both tyres to the same pressure. Bring the car to rest from a forward running position, with the wheels straight ahead.
2 Measure the distance between the tyres or the rims at wheel centre height at the front. Mark these two points of measurement and then roll the car forward for exactly half a revolution of the wheels, so that the marks finish up at the rear. Measure again between the marked points. The difference between the measurements is the amount of toe-in or toe-out.

To adjust the tracking undo locknuts 30 and release the gaiter clips 34. Turn the tie-rods by an equal amount each time. They both have right-hand threads.

Note: The steering rack must be in the central position with the wheels straight ahead. To ensure this the tie-rods must be adjusted to equal lengths, measured from the spanner flats on each rod to the ball-joint locknuts. Screw one rod in and the other out by equal parts of a turn to avoid upsetting the track again. Before tightening the ball-joint locknuts make sure that the joints lie in the same plane relative to each other. Finally, tighten the clips on the gaiters.

Backlash and end play

These can be rectified without removing the rack from the car. Backlash between the pinion and the rack is eliminated by adjusting the position of the damper cap 5. Note that this is actually on the underside of the rack housing. To adjust it proceed as follows:

1 Disconnect the tie-rods from the swivel arms at the extreme outer ends.
2 Remove the steering column clamp bolt 60 and pull the column upwards to free it from the pinion shaft 11.
3 Unscrew the damper cap 5, removing the shims 6 and the plunger spring 4. Place the plunger in the cap without the spring and screw the cap into the housing until it is just possible to rotate the pinion by drawing rack 2 through the housing.
4 **FIG 9:8** shows the next operation. Measure the clearance between the face of the damper cap and the seating in the rack housing with a feeler gauge. Add to this thickness an extra .002 in to .005 in and the sum will be the thickness of shimming required under the damper cap. Shims are available in thicknesses of .003 in and .010 in.
5 Remove the cap and plunger, replace the spring inside the plunger and screw the cap into place with the requisite number of shims.
6 Replace the steering column and tie-rods.
End play of the pinion is rectified in the following way.
1 Repeat the previous operations 1 and 2.
2 Using a dial gauge placed at the splined end of the pinion shaft, check the amount of end play. It should be between .002 in and .005 in. Adjust it by means of shims 13 under the flange of tail bearing 12.
3 Replace the steering column and tie-rods.
Play in the ball-joints 19–23 can be corrected as

follows.
1 Disconnect the tie-rods at the outer ends.
2 Release the gaiter clips 33 and 34. Remove the gaiters 32 having a tin handy to catch the draining oil.
3 Tap back locking washers 31 and unscrew the ball housing 23. Then part the ball housing caps 20 from the housings 23. This will separate the other component parts—the tie-rods 19, the seats 21 and the shims 22.
4 The ball joints must be a reasonably tight sliding fit without play. Adjustment is carried out by varying the thickness of shims. They are available in thicknesses of .002, .003, .005 and .010 in.
5 Refit the completed joints using new lock washers 31 and tapping them over in three places to lock the housing. Replace the gaiters and clips and reconnect the tie-rods to the swivel arms. Replenish the rack housing with the correct Hypoid oil.

Having dealt with adjustments which can be made without removing the rack housing from the car, we now move on to the complete dismantling procedure.

Removing column

1 Detach the negative battery connector.
2 Unscrew nut 61 and remove clamp bolt 60 from the lower splined end of the steering column.
3 Disconnect the horn wire from its snap connection under the fascia.
4 Remove the steering column surround situated between the fascia panel and the steering wheel. This is done by unscrewing three set screws located behind the fascia.
5 Release the two bolts securing the column bracket behind the fascia.
6 The steering wheel and column may now be withdrawn rearwards.
7 Prise out the steering wheel motif and unscrew the wheel securing nut. To avoid damage to the horn switch contact use a socket spanner with a section ground away to clear. Withdraw the steering wheel.

Removing rack

1 In the case of 'Sprite' I remove the radiator as described in the chapter on Cooling.
2 Remove the clamp bolt 60 from the steering column and pull up the column clear of the splines.
3 Detach the tie-rod ball joints 24 from the swivel arms.
4 Remove the set screws 46 which secure the rack housing brackets 40 to the front cross-member. The housing can now be removed complete with brackets and tie-rods.

Dismantling rack

1 Measure and record the distance from the spanner flats on the tie-rods to each of the ball joint locknuts, so that they can be reassembled in the same position.
2 Slacken the ball joint locknuts and unscrew the assemblies from the tie-rods.
3 Remove the gaiters 32 using a tin to catch the oil.
4 Remove the secondary damper 7–10 complete, and the main damper 3–6.
5 Unscrew bolts 14 and take away tail bearing 12 with shims 13. The pinion can now be withdrawn with thrust washer 17. The thicker thrust washer 16 will remain behind and can be removed after the rack is drawn out of the housing.

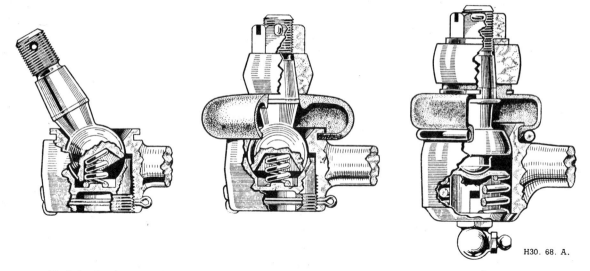

Fig 9:6 Steering connections. Left and centre, the Austin adjustable type. Right, the Lockheed non-adjustable type

H30. 68. A.

6 Tap back locking washers 31 and unscrew the inner ball joints complete. Do not separate the cap 20 from the housing 23 until the complete joint has been unscrewed from the rack.

7 Remove the lock washers and withdraw the rack 2 from the housing 1.

Examine the parts for wear, especially the teeth of the rack and the pinion. If the teeth show signs of roughness or chipping the gears will be unserviceable.

Reassembly

1 Play in the inner ball joints is rectified according to the instructions given earlier. Replace a joint in one end of the rack using a new lock washer, insert the rack in the housing and replace the second joint.

2 Draw the rack through the housing until the centre tooth, which is number 12 from either end, is in the centre of the pinion housing.

3 Place the thicker thrust washer 16 in the rack housing with its chamfered face towards the pinion teeth. Replace the pinion, ensuring that the centre tooth on the rack is in line with the mark on the splined end of the pinion shaft. This must be correct or the steering wheel position will be affected.

4 Replace the thrust washer 17 and the tail bearing 12, using shims 13 to adjust the end play as instructed in an earlier section.

5 Refit the rubber gaiters and clips, renewing a damaged gaiter as it may lead to a loss of oil and the entry of road grit.

6 Screw on the locknuts 30 and fit the outer ball joints in their original positions, using the dimensions taken when dismantling.

7 Replace the main rack damper 3–6, adjusting it with shims as shown in **FIG 9:8**. Also replace the secondary damper 7–10.

8 Fit a new pinion shaft oil seal 18 and pump approximately half a pint of the recommended Hypoid oil into the rack housing.

Replacement

When replacing the rack follow the reverse order of dismantling but do not fully tighten the bracket mounting bolts 46 until the steering column has been fitted and secured to the column support bracket. This ensures correct alignment and the bolts can then be tightened.

Check the tracking and the central position of the rack by referring to the earlier instructions for that operation.

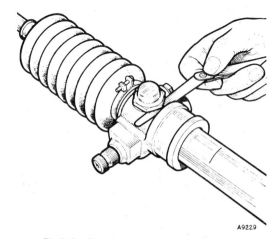

A9229

Fig 9:8 Checking damper cap for shim thickness

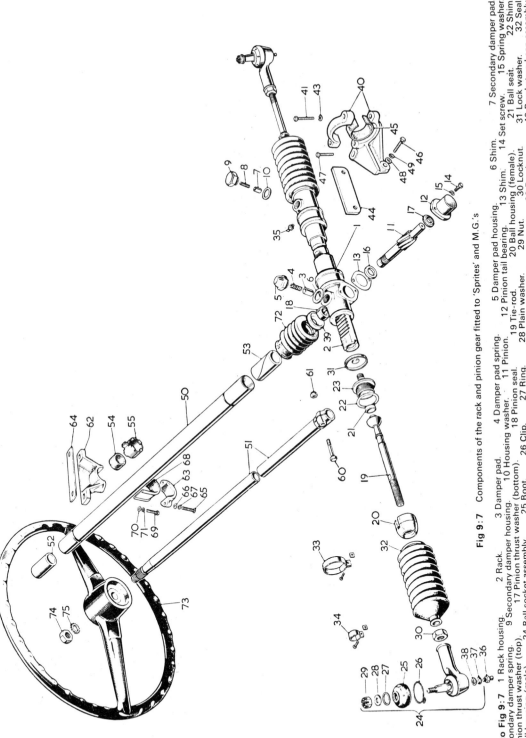

Fig 9:7   Components of the rack and pinion gear fitted to 'Sprites' and M.G.'s

Key to Fig 9:7   1 Rack housing.   2 Rack.   3 Damper pad.   4 Damper pad spring.   5 Damper pad housing.   6 Shim.   7 Secondary damper pad.
8 Secondary damper spring.   9 Secondary damper housing.   10 Housing washer.   11 Pinion.   12 Pinion tail bearing.   13 Shim.   14 Set screw.   15 Spring washer.
16 Pinion thrust washer (top).   17 Pinion thrust washer (bottom).   18 Pinion seal.   19 Tie-rod.   20 Ball housing (female).   21 Ball seat.   22 Shim.
23 Ball housing (male).   24 Ball socket assembly.   25 Boot.   26 Clip.   27 Ring.   28 Plain washer.   29 Nut.   30 Locknut.   31 Lock washer.   32 Seal.
33 Clip (inner).   34 Clip (outer).   35 Lubricator.   36 Packing.   37 Dished washer.   38 Fibre washer.   39 Retainer.   40 Bracket and cap assembly.
41 Set screw.   43 Spring washer.   44 Seating.   45 Packing.   46 Set screw.   47 Set screw.   48 Plain washer.   49 Spring washer.   50 Outer column.
51 Inner column tube.   52 Felt bearing (top).   53 Felt bearing (bottom).   54 Felt bearing (bottom).   55 Clip.   60 Bolt.   61 Nut.   62 Bracket.   63 Bracket cap.
64 Shim.   65 Set screw.   66 Plain washer.   67 Spring washer.   68 Seating.   69 Set screw.   70 Plain washer.   71 Spring washer.   72 Draught excluder.
73 Steering-wheel.   74 Nut.   75 Shakeproof washer.

BMC2

97

FAULT DIAGNOSIS

(a) Wheel wobble

1 Unbalanced wheels and tyres
2 Slack steering connections
3 Incorrect steering geometry
4 Excessive play in steering gear
5 Broken or weak front springs
6 Worn hub bearings

(b) Wander

1 Check 2, 3 and 4 in (a)
2 Front suspension and rear axle mounting points out of line
3 Uneven tyre pressures
4 Uneven tyre wear

5 Weak dampers or springs

(c) Heavy steering

1 Check 3 in (a)
2 Very low tyre pressures
3 Neglected lubrication
4 Out of track
5 Steering gear maladjusted
6 Steering columns bent or misaligned
7 Steering column bushes tight.

(d) Lost motion

1 End play in steering column
2 Loose steering wheel, worn splines
3 Worn steering gearbox and idler
4 Worn ball joints and swivel axle

CHAPTER 10

THE BRAKING SYSTEM

Systems   Operation   Topping-up   Adjustments front and rear   Servicing advice
Servicing front   Servicing rear   Re-lining   Bleeding   Rear cylinder   Master cylinder
Handbrake adjustment   Modifications   Fault diagnosis

The following tables give details of the type of braking system used on each car under review. The particulars for hydraulic front and rear brakes are those for a single brake only.

HYDRAULIC FRONT BRAKES

A30, A35	Two cylinders, two leading shoes, clicker wheel adjustment.
A40, I	Two cylinders, two leading shoes, screw (Micram) adjustment.
A40, II	Two cylinders, two leading shoes, screw (Micram) adjustment.
948-cc 'Sprites' and 'Midgets' ...	Two cylinders, two leading shoes, screw (Micram) adjustment.
1098-cc 'Sprites' and 'Midgets' ...	Disc, no adjustment.

MECHANICAL REAR BRAKES

A30, A35	One hydraulic cylinder operating linkage to mech. brakes, clicker wheel adjustment.
A40, I	One hydraulic cylinder operating linkage to mech. brakes, clicker wheel adjustment.

HYDRAULIC REAR BRAKES

A40, II	One cylinder, two pistons, leading and trailing shoes, backplate adjuster.
948-cc 'Sprites' and 'Midgets' ...	One cylinder, one piston, screw (Micram) adjustment.
1098-cc 'Sprites' and 'Midgets' ...	One cylinder, two pistons, leading and trailing shoes, backplate adjuster.

HANDBRAKE

A30 and A35	Part of hydro-mechanical linkage to rear brake.
A40, I	Part of hydro-mechanical linkage to rear brake.
A40, II	Cable and rods to rear brakes.
'Sprites' I, II and III	Cable and rods to rear brakes.
'Midgets' I and II	Cable and rods to rear brakes.

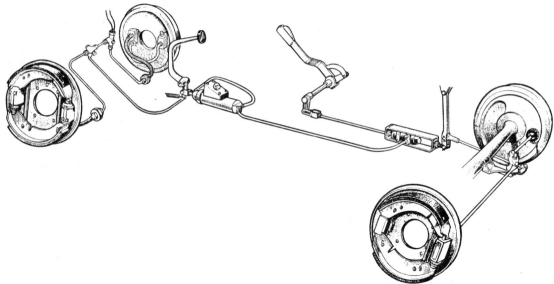

Fig 10:1 Layout of the A30 and A35 braking system

The operating principle behind all the hydraulic systems is the same. It can be followed by examining **FIG 10:1** which shows the layout of the braking system on A30's and A35's. Note, however, that the hydraulic cylinder to be seen in the middle of the handbrake linkage is peculiar to these cars and to the A40, I. Later cars have a hydraulic cylinder inside each rear brake. The brake pedal is connected to the piston of a master pumping cylinder, **FIG 10:16.** This is connected by pipes to the brake shoe operating cylinders, see item 10 in **FIG 10:4,** the whole system being full of fluid. Depressing the brake pedal causes the master cylinder piston to force fluid along the pipelines into the wheel cylinders. Here, other pistons are thrust outwards, pushing the brake shoes into contact with the drums. When the pedal is released strong springs across the shoes push the brake pistons back into their bores thus forcing the fluid back into the master cylinder.

Topping-up

Never let the fluid level in the master cylinder reservoir fall too low or air may enter the system, making it necessary to bleed it. Air is compressible and gives a 'spongy' feeling to the brakes.

The filler cap is on top of the master cylinder reservoir. Clean all round it before unscrewing. Fill to within $\frac{1}{4}$ in of the bottom of the filler neck, using Lockheed Super Heavy Duty Fluid only. If this is not available, no other fluid is permissible except one which conforms with Specification S.A.E. 70R3. For 1098-cc 'Sprites' and 'Midgets', use Lockheed Disc Brake Fluid. A substitute will seriously affect the working of the system.

Adjustment—front brakes—A30 and A35

When adjusting brakes, do the complete set and not just one brake alone.

1 Apply the handbrake, jack up a wheel and remove the hub cap.

2 Spin the wheel and apply the footbrake firmly to centralise the brake shoes.

3 Align the holes in wheel and drum with one of the clicker wheels 10 in **FIG 10:2**. With a screwdriver, turn the clicker wheel clockwise relative to the cylinder until the brake shoe is hard against the drum. Back off two or three clicks until the drum is just free. Repeat on the second cylinder.

Adjustment—front brakes—A40, I and II 948-cc 'Sprites' and 'Midgets'

Repeat 1 and 2 above.

3 Find the screw of one of the 'Micram' adjusters shown in **FIG 10:3** and turn it clockwise until the shoe locks the drum. Back off one notch. Repeat on the second cylinder of the same brake.

Adjustment—rear brakes—A30, A35 and A40, I

1 Place chocks under the front wheels and release the handbrake. Jack up one of the rear wheels and remove the hub cap.

2 Turn the single clicker wheel as for the front brake, but back off a little more as this adjusts the clearance of two shoes. The clicker wheel is item 4 in **FIG 10:5**. Repeat on the other brake. This adjustment sets the handbrake too, and normally no other adjustment is needed.

Adjustment—rear brakes—A40, II, 1098-cc 'Sprites' and 'Midgets'

1 Repeat 1 in the previous section.

2 Locate the adjuster shown in **FIG 10:6** and turn it clockwise to lock the brake drum. Back off until the drum is just free when rotated.

Adjustment—rear brakes—948-cc 'Sprites' and 'Midgets'

These have the single adjuster shown in **FIG 10:7**. Turn clockwise as before and back off two notches.

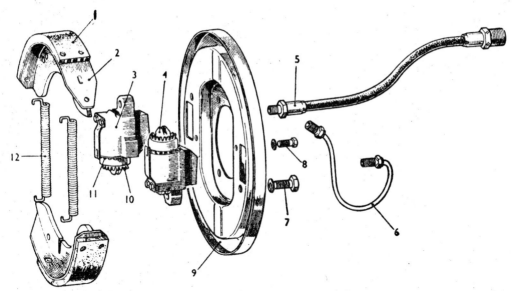

Fig 10:2 The left-hand front brake assembly on the A30 and A35

Key to Fig 10:2 1 Brake lining. 2 Brake shoe. 3 Wheel cylinder. 4 Slotted adjusting screw. 5 Flexible brake hose.
6 Cylinder interconnecting bridge pipe. 7 Cylinder fixing bolt (large). 8 Cylinder fixing bolt (small). 9 Backplate.
10 Clicker wheel. 11 Dust cover. 12 Pull-off springs.

IMPORTANT

Before describing the dismantling of the various hydraulic systems, a few general points will be mentioned here to avoid too much repetition.

Leakage past the pistons in hydraulic cylinders is prevented by rubber seals. These have a raised lip which presses firmly against the polished cylinder bore. As the lip faces fluid pressure, the greater the pressure the stronger the seal. From this, it will be appreciated that the seals and the bores must be in perfect condition and also spotlessly clean. To ensure this, it is necessary to remove all outside dirt before dismantling any hydraulic parts. After dismantling, wash the rubber parts in clean brake fluid and no other liquid. If metal parts are washed in solvent liquids such as petrol, all traces must be dried off before reassembling.

It is advisable to replace all old seals with new ones, and most certainly if there has been leakage. To avoid damage, remove and replace the seals with the fingers.

Start reassembly by lubricating all the parts with correct brake fluid and assemble wet.

When replacing the rubber seals in the cylinder bores, enter the raised lip first and make sure that it is not trapped or turned back on itself.

If the brake shoes are removed from the backplate at any time, be very careful not to depress the footbrake pedal or the wheel cylinder pistons will be forced out of the bores. It is a good idea to prevent this by wiring the pistons or by fitting a clamp over them.

Dismantling—front brakes—A30 and A35

1 Jack up the car, remove the wheel, back off all adjustment and take off the drum.

2 Pull one of the shoes 2 outwards against the load of springs 12, as seen in **FIG 10:2**. Disengage the shoe from the slots in adjuster screw 4 and from the other wheel cylinder. The tension on the springs can now be eased and the other shoe removed. Unscrew the flexible hose 5.

Note: This type of hose is common to all models and there is a correct sequence for removing it if damage is to be avoided. Never start by attempting to unscrew the outer end from the brake cylinder. First unscrew the union nut on the metal pipeline, seen as item 1 in **FIG 10:8**. Hold the hexagon on the flexible hose and unscrew the locknut 2 which secures the hose to its mounting bracket. With the inner end now free the hose can be unscrewed from the wheel cylinder where it protrudes through the backplate. Always refit in the reverse order.

3 Dismantle the cylinders using **FIG 10:9** for reference. Remove screws 5 and clicker spring 4. Withdraw piston 3 complete with adjusting screw 9, clicker wheel 1, dust cover 2 and tapered seal 7.

4 Clean all the parts as suggested in the notes at the beginning of the section on dismantling. Then reassemble, screwing in adjuster 9 all the way.

5 Refit the cylinders to the backplate. Attach the springs to the shoes in the position shown in **FIG 10:2**. Engage the lower shoe in the slots of the adjuster and the cylinder, tension the springs by pulling the other shoe and allow it to return into the second pair of slots.

6 Refit the hose and bridge pipe. Bleed the system.

Dismantling—front brakes—A40, I and II 948-cc 'Sprites' and 'Midgets'

1 Reaching the point where the drum has been removed, pull one of the brake shoes against the load of springs 7 in **FIG 10:4** until it is clear of the abutment slot on

cylinder 10. Slide the 'Micram' mask 9 off the piston cover 11 of the opposite cylinder, release the tension on the springs and take away both shoes.

2 Remove the flexible hose, detach the bridge pipe, unscrew the cylinder bolts and remove the cylinders from the front.

3 Dismantle the cylinders by removing the dust cover if one is fitted, withdrawing the piston 11, the sealing cup 12, the filler 13 and the spring 14. The parts may differ on some models but the principle remains the same.

4 To reassemble, follow the sequence given for the A30 and A35.

Dismantling—front brakes—1098-cc 'Sprites' and 'Midgets'

The left-hand side of **FIG 10 : 4** shows the components of the disc brakes fitted to the front wheels of later 'Sprites' and 'Midgets'. The calliper body 30 is bolted to the axle stub and embraces the edge of the disc 24. Each half of the calliper contains a hydraulic cylinder bore with a piston 31 and seals against leakage and dust 32 and 33. The pistons press on the friction-lined pads 34 simultaneously when the brake pedal is applied. Thus the disc is nipped between the braking surfaces, giving a powerful retarding action.

1 Having removed the road wheel, disconnect the fluid supply hose.

2 Unscrew the nuts securing the hose retaining plate to the calliper assembly.

3 Remove the studs holding the calliper to the stub axle and withdraw it.

4 Depress the pad retaining springs 35 and pull out split pins 36. Remove the friction pads 34 and anti-squeak shims 37. Clean the outside of the callipers thoroughly, removing every trace of cleaning fluid afterwards.

5 Reconnect the supply hose, supporting the calliper so that the hose is not strained. Put a clamp on the inner piston and apply the footbrake gently. This will eject the outer piston until it can be withdrawn by hand. Have a clean tin ready to catch the draining fluid.

6 Use a blunt-nosed tool to remove the inner seal 32 from its groove in the bore, taking care not to damage any part. Prise out the dust seal and its retainer 33 from the mouth of the bore.

7 To extract the inner piston, remove the clamp and after replacing and clamping the outer piston, use the footbrake again.

8 If it is necessary to remove the disc 24, refit it by following the instructions given in the Front Suspension chapter.

Reassembling—front brakes—1098-cc 'Sprites' and 'Midgets'

1 Dry a new seal 32 then coat it with Lockheed Disc Brake Lubricant and ease it with the fingers into the groove in the bore of one of the callipers.

2 Slacken the bleed screw 39 one turn. Smear the piston with Lubricant and place in the bore squarely and with the cut-away on the face positioned downwards.

3 Press in the piston until about $\frac{5}{16}$ in is left protruding. If the dust seal and retainer 33 were removed, fit a new seal into the retainer, drying it first and then smearing it with Lubricant. Place over the piston with the seal innermost. Keeping everything square with the bore,

use a clamp to press home the piston and seal. Retighten the bleed screw then repeat for the other calliper. When dealing with the inner calliper it is necessary to remove the flexible hose so that a clamp can be used.

4 Reconnect the hose and bolt the calliper assembly to the stub axle. Do not depress the brake pedal until the pad assemblies, retaining springs and split pins 36 have been replaced. Then bleed the system according to the instructions given later in this chapter. After this, depress the brake pedal several times until it feels 'solid'. No further adjustment is needed.

Dismantling—rear brakes—A30 and A35

The internal mechanism of these brakes is purely mechanical, as can be seen from **FIG 10 : 5**. The pull-rod 6 is connected to a lever in the expander unit 12. Pulling the rod moves a slotted lever outwards (item 1 in **FIG 10 : 10**). In the slot is the toe of one of the brake shoes, the heel resting in the abutment 10. The heel of the lower shoe rests in the slotted head of the adjuster screw 3. The expander unit is free to float in a slot in the back-plate. When the slotted lever forces the top shoe against the drum, the expander unit reacts downwards to apply the lower shoe.

Dismantle the shoes as instructed for the front brakes, tap out pin 8 and withdraw the expander unit. Dismantle it as follows:

1 Tap out pin 7 in **FIG 10 : 10** and withdraw outer lever 6 and inner lever 1. Hold back the clicker spring and unscrew the adjuster screw 11 and wheel 12.

Reassembling unit

1 Smear the parts with Lockheed Expander Lubricant.

2 Assemble the outer lever 6 and inner lever 1 on the bench, securing the parts with pin 10. Insert the assembly in the body, fitting pin 7. Replace the adjuster screw in the adjuster wheel, screwing it right home, then hold back the clicker spring and insert in the body.

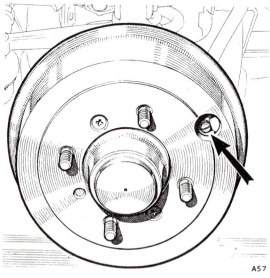

A57

Fig 10 : 3 One of the two front brake adjusters, A40 I and II, 'Sprites' I and II, 'Midget' I

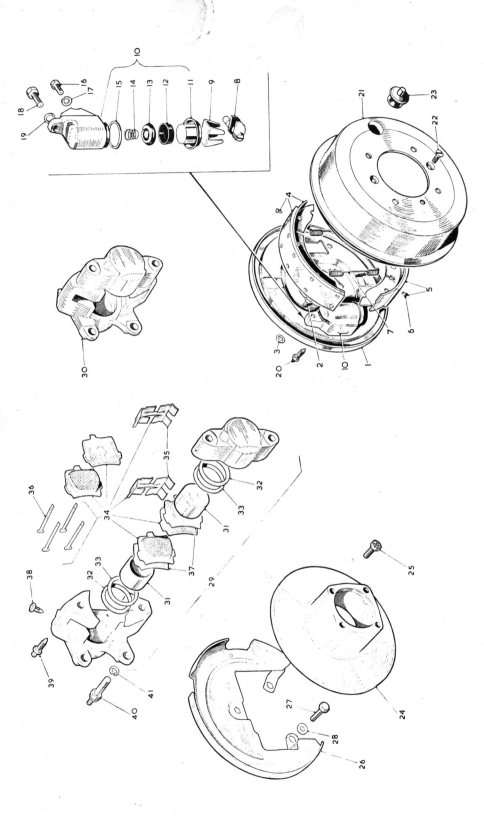

Fig 10:4   Components of front disc brakes for 1098 cc 'Sprites' and 'Midgets' (left). Front drum brake parts for all models except A30 and A35 (right)

Key to Fig 10:4   1 Brake plate   2 Set screw.   3 Shakeproof washer.   4 Brake-shoe assembly.   5 Liner with rivets.   6 Rivet.   7 Pull-off spring.
8 Micram adjuster.   9 Mask.   10 Wheel cylinder assembly.   11 Piston with dust cover.   12 Cup.   13 Cup filler.   14 Spring.   15 Sealing ring.
16 Set screw (small).   17 Spring washer.   18 Set screw (large).   19 Spring washer.   20 Bleeder screw.   21 Brake-drum.   22 Set screw.   23 Plug.
24 Brake disc.   25 Set screw.   26 Dust cover.   27 Set screw.   28 Shakeproof washer.   29 Calliper unit assembly—L.H.   30 Calliper—L.H.   31 Piston.
32 Inner seal.   33 Dust seal and retainer.   34 Pad assembly.   35 Pad retaining spring.   36 Split cotter pin.   37 Pad shim.   38 Plug.   39 Bleed screw.
40 Calliper mounting bolt.   41 Spring washer.

Reassembling—rear brakes—A30, A35 and A40, I

1 Locate the expander unit in the backplate with the clicker spring facing inwards. Replace pin 8.
2 Assemble the shoes and springs according to **FIG 10:5**. Note that the expander unit fits in the slot behind spring guide 11 to engage the ends of the shoes farthest away in the illustration. The sharply tapered toe of one shoe faces the blunter heel of the other. The toe of the upper shoe will now enter lever 1 in **FIG 10:10**, the heel of the other shoe dropping into the slot of adjusting screw 3 in **FIG 10:5**. The opposite ends fit in abutment 10. Spring 14 must be located within guide 11. The coil of spring 13 faces inwards.

Dismantling—rear brakes—948-cc 'Sprites' and 'Midgets'

FIG 10:11 shows in 'ghosted' fashion the single hydraulic cylinder fitted to the rear brake. There is also only one piston 13. This cylinder is free to float, the piston pushing out one shoe and the cylinder body, by reaction, pushing out the other. An outer piston 14 is a distance piece between the hydraulic piston 13 and the shoe 6. Piston 14 is slotted to take the tapered end of handbrake lever 19. Operation of the handbrake pushes piston 14 outwards to expand the shoes, leaving piston 13 undisturbed.

1 Remove the wheel, drum and axle shaft as described in the Rear Axle and Suspension chapter.
2 Working behind the backplate, disconnect the flexible hose and the handbrake lever rod. Remove the backplate.

3 Pull the shoes away from their abutments as previously described. This will release the springs, the 'Micram' mask 12 and the adjuster 11.
4 Remove the banjo bolt from the hose adaptor on the wheel cylinder, and the rubber boot 21.
5 Remove the cylinder by swinging the handbrake lever until the shoulder is clear of the backplate. Slide the cylinder forward. Pivot the cylinder about its forward end and withdraw the rear end from the slot. A rearward movement of the cylinder will then bring the forward end clear of the backplate.
6 Withdraw the outer piston 14 and pivot pin 20, enabling lever 19 to be withdrawn. Apply gentle air pressure to the fluid entry on the cylinder and blow out hydraulic piston 13, rubber cup 16, filler 17 and spring 18.

Reassembling—rear brakes—948-cc 'Sprites' and 'Midgets'

1 Back off all adjusters.
2 Ensure that the slots in the pistons coincide with lever 19 when fitted in the cylinder.
3 Use **FIG 10:11** to follow the correct assembly of the shoes and the adjuster. Note that the farthest tip of top shoe 6 has the lining cut well back. It also has a recess for the adjuster 11. The nearest end of shoe 7 also has the lining cut back. This end fits against the abutment block on the backplate. Springs 8 and 9 are shown as they must be assembled. The coils lie between the shoes and the backplate.

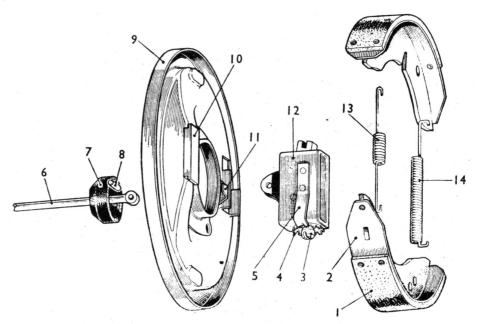

Fig 10:5   Left-hand rear brake assembly on the A30, A35 and A40, I

Key to Fig 10:5   1 Brake lining.   2 Brake shoe.   3 Slotted adjusting screw.   4 Adjuster wheel.   5 Clicker spring.
6 Pull-rod.   7 Rubber boot.   8 Pin.   9 Backplate.   10 Abutment pad.   11 Spring guide.   12 Expander unit.
13 Pull-off spring (short coil).   14 Pull-off spring (long coil).

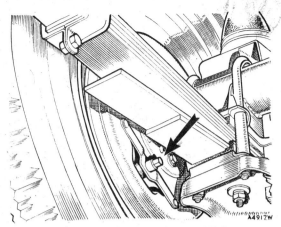

Fig 10:6 Rear brake adjustment, A40 II

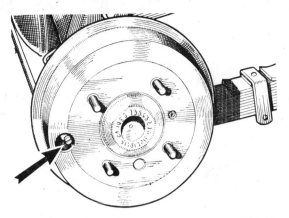

Fig 10:7 Single rear brake adjuster on 'Sprite' I, early 'Sprite' II and 'Midget' I

Dismantling—rear brakes—1098-cc 'Sprites' and 'Midgets', A40, II

The left-hand section of **FIG 10:11** shows the rear brake components for these later cars. The single hydraulic cylinder is shown 'ghosted'. It carries two working pistons back to back. These push outwards on the ends of the brake shoes. Unlike the floating cylinder on the earlier models, this cylinder is secured to the backplate. The adjuster 25 is screwed into the backplate and has a tapered end. When the adjuster is screwed in, the taper expands the ends of the shoes through the agency of tappets 24.

1 Follow the instructions for dismantling the earlier type described in the previous section, but after detaching the flexible hose, unscrew and remove the bleed screw. Take off circlip 31 and dished washer 30 from the cylinder boss where it protrudes through the backplate. Dismantle the cylinder as already described.

Brake linings

As it is possible to buy replacement shoes with new linings properly fitted it is really not advisable to attempt the relining process. Specialist facilities are needed to ensure that the linings are concentric with the drums. If the linings are not tightly bedded down on the shoes there can also be trouble from 'spongy' brakes.

Always fit complete sets, using the specified grade of lining material or there will be out-of-balance braking effects.

Do not attempt to clean oily linings as nothing permanent can be done. When fitting shoes which have new linings, turn the adjusters to the fully 'off' position first, and release the handbrake.

Renewing disc pads

1 Jack up the car and remove the road wheel.
2 Depress the pad retaining spring 35 in **FIG 10:4** and withdraw the split pins 36. Remove the spring and withdraw the pads 34 and shims 37 by rotating slightly. Use a pair of long-nosed pliers for this operation.
3 Clean the piston faces and the calliper recesses, then press each piston back into the calliper. This will cause a rise in the master cylinder fluid level and it may be necessary to syphon some off.

4 Check that the relieved face of each piston is correctly positioned and fit the new pad assemblies with the anti-squeak shims between pad and piston.
5 The pad assemblies must move freely in the calliper recesses. Remove highspots from the pad pressure plate by judicious filing.
6 Refit the retaining spring, press it down and insert new split pins. Renew springs which are damaged or weak.
7 Operate the brake pedal several times until the brake feels 'solid' and then top-up the master cylinder.

Bleeding the brakes

This operation is necessary if any of the hydraulic pipelines or unions have been disconnected, or if the fluid level in the master cylinder reservoir has fallen so low that air has entered the system. The presence of air is usually shown by a 'spongy' feeling of the brake pedal and loss of braking power. After complete dismantling, more than one reservoir full of fluid may be needed to refill the system. The operator should therefore have sufficient fluid available to keep the reservoir topped-up throughout the process of bleeding. If the fluid level in the reservoir drops so low that air can enter the system, it will be necessary to make a fresh start.

1 With every hydraulic connection secure and the supply reservoir topped-up with the correct grade of fluid, remove the rubber cap from the rear bleed nipple farthest from the master cylinder, see item 29 in **FIG 10:11**. The bleed nipples will always be found behind the backplate, where the flexible hose or bridge pipe is connected. If there is no rubber cap, clean the nipple thoroughly before the next operation.

Fit a rubber or plastic tube over the nipple and immerse the free end in a small quantity of fluid in a clean jar.

2 Unscrew the nipple part of a turn and get a second operator to depress the brake pedal steadily through a full stroke. Fluid and air bubbles will be seen coming out of the tube in the jar. Continue the slow steady strokes, pausing when the pedal is right back to allow the master cylinder to fill. Do this until fluid without a trace of air bubbles is seen to emerge into the jar. Then, during a down stroke of the pedal, tighten the bleed

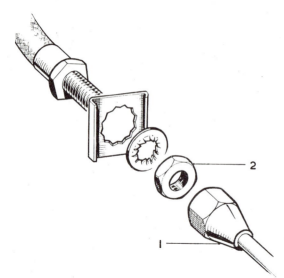

Fig 10:8   Removing flexible hoses. Unscrew union 1, then nut 2 from inner end, finally unscrew hose at outer end

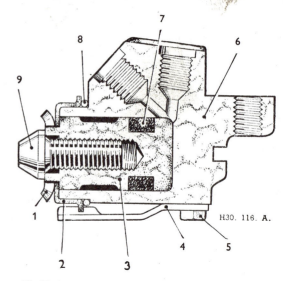

Fig 10:9   Front wheel cylinder in section, A30 and A35

Key to Fig 10:9   1 Clicker wheel.   2 Dust cover.   3 Piston.
4 Clicker spring.   5 Screws.   6 Body.   7 Taper seal.
8 Dust sealing ring.   9 Slotted adjusting screw.

screw moderately. Excessive force is undesirable.

3 Repeat the process on the other three brakes, finishing at the wheel nearest to the master cylinder. On the A30, A35 and A40, I, there are no bleed nipples on the rear brakes, but a single one on the operating cylinder under the car, see **FIG 10:12**, item 17.

Keep checking the fluid level in the master cylinder reservoir so that it never becomes empty at any time. Finally, top-up to the required level.

Fluid which has been bled into the jar will be dirty and aerated and should not be used again. If its cleanliness is beyond dispute it can be de-aerated by leaving it to stand for twenty-four hours.

Rear brake cylinder—A30, A35 and A40, I

This hydraulic cylinder operates the rear brakes through a linkage which also forms part of the handbrake mechanism. The layout for the A30 and A35 is shown in **FIG 10:12**, the cylinder being item 17. **FIG 10:13** shows the layout for the A40, I. In this, the cylinder is shown in section in the bottom left-hand corner, and again in **FIG 10:14**. The cylinder is bolted to a bracket on the underside of the car body. A push-rod 4 is fixed to stirrup 23 (**FIG 10:12**), so that depression of the brake pedal moves both push-rod and stirrup forward to apply the rear brakes through a mechanical linkage. A slot in the handbrake linkage can be seen in item 15, **FIG 10:12**, and as an inset in **FIG 10:13**. This allows the footbrake mechanism to work without affecting the handbrake. When the handbrake is applied the closed end of the slot pulls the linkage in the same direction as it would if the footbrake pedal had been used. The diagrammatic views in **FIG 10:15** show this principle clearly.

Dismantling

1 Disconnect the cylinder from the body bracket and from the stirrup and linkage. Unscrew the pipe connection.

2 Peel back the boot 5 in **FIG 10:14** and remove it together with the push rod 4. Blow out the piston parts 1, 2, 3 and 7 with gentle air pressure.

Reassembling

1 Insert spring 1 with large end first. Follow with expander 2 and rubber cup 3 with lip leading. Take care not to trap or turn back this lip.

2 Insert piston 7 with its flat surface leading. Fit the small end of the boot to the push-rod, insert the rod in the bore and fit the large end of the boot to the groove in the body.

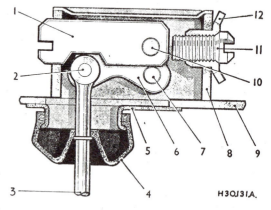

Fig 10:10   Rear brake expander unit, A30, A35 and A40, I

Key to Fig 10:10   1 Inner lever.   2 Pull-rod pin.   3 Pull-rod.
4 Rubber boot.   5 Dust cover.   6 Outer lever.   7 Pin.
lever to body.   8 Expander body.   9 Backplate.   10 Inner and outer lever securing pin.   11 Slotted adjuster screw.
12 Adjuster wheel.

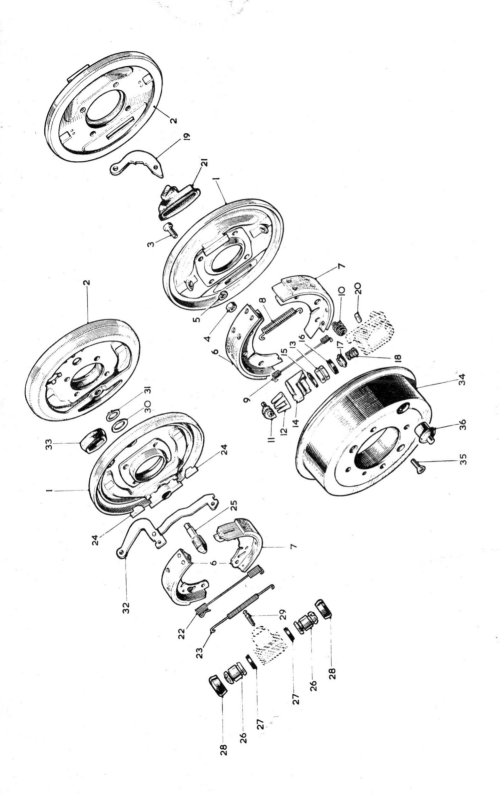

Fig 10:11 Rear brake components. A40 II, 1098 cc 'Sprites' and 'Midgets' (left), 948 cc 'Sprites' and 'Midgets' (right)

Key to Fig 10:11 1 Brake-plate — R.H. 2 Brake-plate — L.H. 3 Set screw. 4 Nut. 5 Spring washer. 6 Brake-shoe assembly. 7 Liner with rivets.
8 Shoe return spring (abutment end). 9 Shoe return spring (cylinder end). 10 Steady spring. 11 Adjuster assembly. 12 Mask adjuster. 13 Piston.
14 Piston with dust cover. 15 Seal. 16 Cup. 17 Cup filler. 18 Spring. 19 Hand brake lever. 20 Pivot pin. 21 Boot. 22 Shoe return spring (cylinder end).
23 Shoe return spring (adjuster end). 24 Tappet. 25 Wedge. 26 Piston. 27 Seal. 28 Boot. 29 Bleeder screw. 30 Belleville washer. 31 Circlip.
32 Handbrake lever. 33 Boot. 34 Brake-drum. 35 Set screw. 36 Plug.

3 Refit the cylinder, drawing the push-rod back a little to allow the fixing bolts a clear passage through the body.

4 Adjust the linkage by working on the stirrup linkage so that all slackness is taken out without actually operating the rear brake expander rods. Too close an adjustment may cause the rear brakes to drag. It is essential that there is a clearance of approximately $\frac{1}{16}$ in in the handbrake sliding link. This is shown in the inset to **FIG 10:13**.

Master cylinder—all models

The working principles and internal parts of the various master cylinders are much the same throughout. There are differences in location and in some cases the clutch and brake cylinders are combined in a common casting, but the instructions for working on the internal parts will do for all models. The action of the cylinder can be seen by examining **FIG 10:16**. Push-rod 6 is connected to the brake pedal and moves inwards when the pedal is depressed. This pushes piston 10 up the bore. Fluid leakage past the piston is prevented by rubber seals 12 and 9. The supply tank 3 contains the main supply of fluid and the bore of the cylinder and the whole of the system is kept full of fluid by entry through a small hole to be seen just in front of the lip of seal 12. This hole is cut off as soon as the piston starts to move inwards. Fluid is forced along the bore and into the braking system past a valve assembly 16. This valve normally opens when fluid flows in both directions. Its function is to prevent fluid pumped into the system during the operation of bleeding the brakes from returning into the master cylinder, which will then take a fresh charge of fluid from the supply reservoir.

Removing master cylinder—A30 and A35

1 The cylinder is under the floor behind the brake pedal. Disconnect the two pipes from the rear end of the cylinder.

2 Unscrew the pedal pad. Release the fixing nuts and remove the pedal and cylinder assembly.

Removing master cylinder—A40, I and II

1 The clutch and brake master cylinders are mounted separately under the bonnet and over the pedals. Check carefully which cylinder is used for the brakes and then remove the circlip which secures the pedal cross shaft. An illustration of the pedal assembly will be found in the Clutch chapter.

2 Push off the hooked ends of the pedal return spring. Take out the cross-shaft and then detach the push-rod from the pedal arm.

3 Disconnect the pipe from the top of the cylinder, remove the securing nuts and withdraw the cylinder complete.

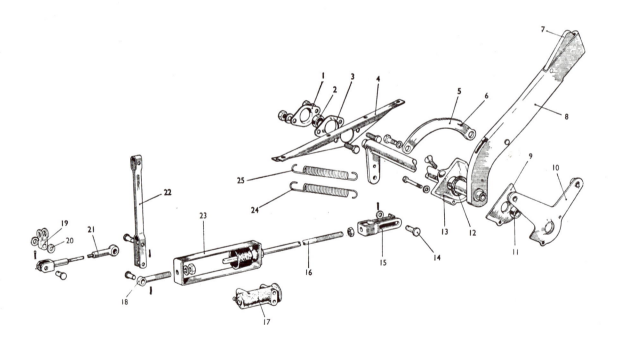

Fig 10:12   Handbrake assembly on A30 and A35

Key to Fig 10:12   1 Flange for spherical bush.   2 Spherical bush.   3 Flange for spherical bush.   4 Cross-shaft support bracket.
5 Quadrant.   6 Stop peg.   7 Trigger.   8 Handbrake lever.   9 Outer bush flange.   10 Quadrant bracket.   11 Spherical bush.
12 Felt washer.   13 Support flange.   14 Sliding link joint pin.   15 Sliding link.   16 Handbrake rod.   17 Rear cylinder body.
18 Eye-rod for stirrup.   19 Link to balance lever.   20 Felt washers.   21 Rear brake cable.   22 Rear brake link.   23 Stirrup.
24 Rod pull-off spring.   25 Lever pull-off spring.

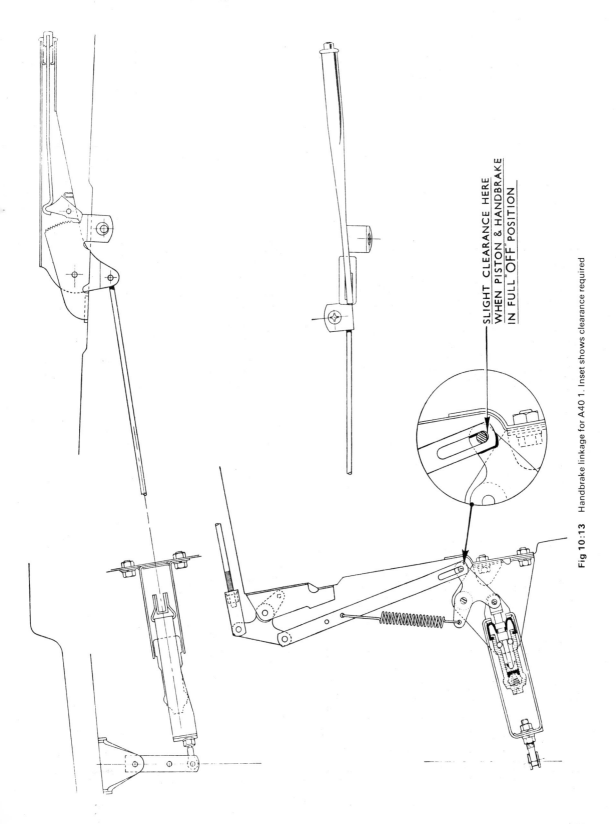

SLIGHT CLEARANCE HERE
WHEN PISTON & HANDBRAKE
IN FULL "OFF" POSITION

Fig 10:13   Handbrake linkage for A40 1. Inset shows clearance required

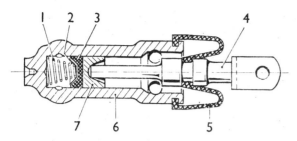

Fig 10:14 Rear brake cylinder in section, A30, A35 and A40 I

Key to Fig 10:14 1 Expander spring.   2 Cup expander.
3 Rubber cup.   4 Push rod.   5 Rubber boot.   6 Body.
7 Piston.

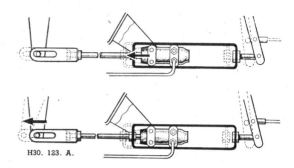

H30. 123. A.

Fig 10:15 Rear brake action on A30, A35 and A40 I. Top:
brake pedal operation. Bottom: handbrake operation

Removing master cylinder—
'Sprites' I, II and III. 'Midgets' I and II

1 Follow the instructions in the Clutch chapter for removing the master cylinder unit with pedals.
2 Disconnect each pedal from its push-rod. Remove the
bolts holding the unit to the mounting plate.

Dismantling master cylinder—all models

1 On the double master cylinders remove the boot fixing
plate 15 in **FIG 10:17**, the boots 18 and push-rods 19.
2 On single installations remove the boot 5 and then the
circlip 7 in **FIG 10:16** followed by washer 8 and push-
rod 6.
3 Invert the cylinder and tap out the internal parts, all of
which can be recognised in **FIGS 10:16** and **10:17**.
There may be slight differences in the design of the
valve, and the A30 and A35 may be found to have a
rubber valve seat at the extreme end of the bore, but
there should be no difficulty in identifying the equivalent parts.
Clean and reassemble as instructed earlier, using correct

brake fluid as a lubricant. Take care to fit the sealing cups
with the lips entering the bore first. The vent holes in the
boots of twin units should be fitted so that they are below
when mounted in the car.

Handbrake adjustment—
A40, II. 'Sprites' I, II and III. 'Midgets' I and II

The handbrake on these cars is connected by cable to
the compensator mounted on the rear axle, see **FIG 10:18**
for the 'Sprites' and 'Midgets' and **FIG 10:19** for the A40,
II. Running from the compensator to the rear brake levers
are non-adjustable transverse rods. Normally, no adjustment is required but a complete overhaul may make it
necessary.

1 Lock the rear brake shoes to the drums by means of the
adjusters on each backplate.
2 Apply the handbrake slightly and just remove any cable
slackness by means of the adjustments shown in **FIGS
10:18** and **10:19**. Lubricate the balance lever by means
of the nipple on top and oil the clevis pins and joints of
the transverse rods and cable fork. The cable grease
nipple is just forward of the rear axle.

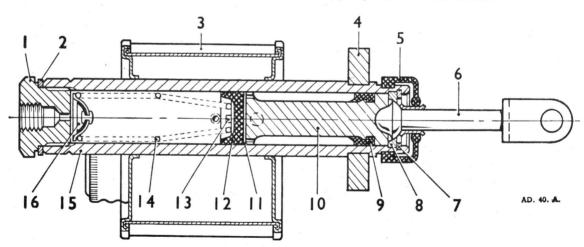

Fig 10:16 Sectional view of A40 master cylinder

Key to Fig 10:16 1 End plug.   2 Washer.   3 Supply tank.   4 Mounting flange.   5 Rubber boot.   6 Push rod.   7 Circlip.
8 Stop washer.   9 Secondary cup.   10 Piston.   11 Piston washer.   12 Main cup.   13 Spring retainer.   14 Return spring.
15 Body.   16 Valve assembly.

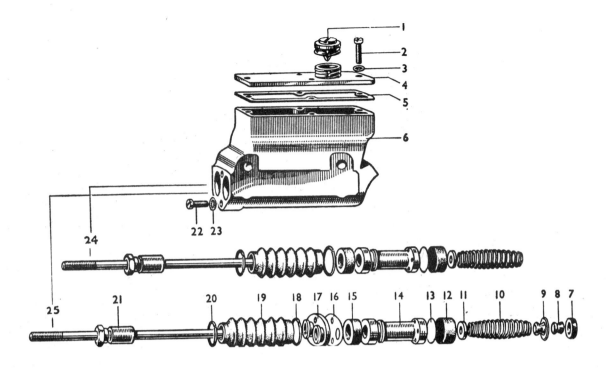

Fig 10:17 Double-bore master cylinder on 'Sprite I'. Later 'Sprites' and 'Midgets' differ only in small details

Key to Fig 10:17 1 Filler cap.   2 Fixing screw.   3 Shakeproof washer.   4 Tank cover.   5 Tank cover gasket.
6 Cylinder barrel and tank.   7 Valve washer.   8 Valve cup.   9 Valve body.   10 Return spring.   11 Spring retainer.
12 Main cup.   13 Piston washer.   14 Piston.   15 Secondary cup.   16 Gasket.   17 Boot fixing plate.   18 Boot clip.
19 Boot.   20 Boot clip.   21 Push-rod.   22 Fixing screw.   23 Shakeproof washer.   24 Clutch bore.   25 Brake bore.

Brake pedal clearance

The correct amount of free movement between the master cylinder push-rod and the piston is set during manufacture and should not need alteration. If the adjustment has been disturbed, reset the effective length of the rod connecting the piston to the pedal. Adjust until the pedal pad can be depressed about $\frac{5}{32}$ in before the piston begins to move. This clearance can be felt if the pedal is depressed by hand. It is most important that the push-rod should have a minimum free movement of $\frac{1}{32}$ in before the piston starts to move.

Modifications

On the A40, I system which has a cylinder for operating the rear brakes, a modification was introduced to exclude the possibility of corrosion. From Car No. 22523, copper packings were added between each side of the cylinder and its mounting bracket. They were also fitted under the mounting bolts and nuts. Plain washers under the nuts face on to the new packings and the bolts were increased in length.

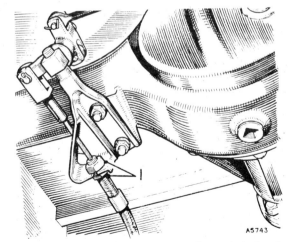

Fig 10:18 Location of handbrake adjustment, 'Sprites' and 'Midgets'

FAULT DIAGNOSIS

(a) 'Spongy' pedal

1 Leak in the system
2 Wear of the master cylinder and bore
3 Leaking wheel cylinders
4 Air in the system
5 Gaps between the underside of linings and the shoes

(b) Excessive pedal movement

1 Check 1 and 4 in (a)
2 Excessive lining wear
3 Very low fluid level in supply reservoir
4 Too much free movement of pedal

(c) Brakes grab or pull to one side

1 Brake backplate loose
2 Scored, cracked or distorted drum
3 Highspots on drum
4 Unbalanced shoe adjustment
5 Wet or oily linings
6 Worn or loose rear spring fixings
7 Front suspension or rear axle anchorages loose
8 Worn steering connections
9 Mixed linings of different grades
10 Uneven tyre pressures
11 Broken shoe return springs
12 Seized handbrake cable

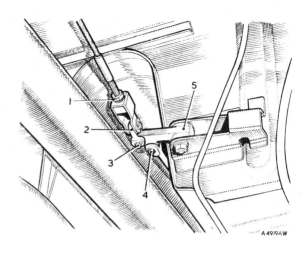

Fig 10:19   Handbrake adjuster and lubricating points, A40 II

Key to Fig 10:19   1 Cable adjuster.   2 Cable joint pin.
3 Link pin.   4 Rod joint pin.   5 Intermediate lever pivot pin.

CHAPTER 11

THE ELECTRICAL SYSTEM

Battery   Generator   Generator servicing   Starter   Starter servicing   Control box
Regulator setting   Cut-out setting   Fuses   Headlamps   Wipers   Fuel gauge
Flasher units   Fault diagnosis

All the models covered by this manual have 12-volt electrical systems in which the positive battery terminal is earthed. There is a regulator in the control box which gives compensated voltage control of the charging circuit to prevent damage to the battery by over-charging.

Both headlamps use the double-filament dipping system and later headlamps have sealed beam units.

There are wiring diagrams in the Technical Data section to enable those with some electrical experience to trace and correct wiring faults.

Serious mechanical and electrical defects in the generator and starter motor are best cured by fitting new units on an Exchange basis, but instructions for those adjustments which can be made by a reasonably competent engineer have been included in this chapter. To carry out such adjustments to the electrical control gear demands the use of precise measuring instruments. Unreliable instruments will make accurate adjustment impossible.

The battery

This is a 12-volt lead-acid type using dilute sulphuric acid as an electrolyte. The life of a battery is a hard one and it will be considerably shortened by the lack of regular maintenance. An obvious sign of trouble is corrosion of the terminals and surrounding parts. This causes both electrical resistance and electrical leakage. Clean off the corrosion by washing with dilute ammonia then dry the parts and smear the terminal posts with petroleum jelly. Use anti-sulphuric paint on adjacent metal parts such as the battery bolts, the strap and the tray. The top of the battery must always be dry and clean. Dampness encour-

ages the spread of corrosion and provides a path for electrical leakage.

The electrolyte

The level must be maintained just above the tops of the separators. Never add acid but top-up with distilled water. The condition of the battery can be checked by measuring the Specific Gravity of the electrolyte in each cell with a hydrometer. The indications are as follows:

For climates below 27°C or 80°F

Cell fully charged ...	Specific Gravity 1.270 to 1.290
Cell half-discharged	1.190 to 1.210
Cell fully discharged	1.110 to 1.130

These figures are for an electrolyte temperature of 16°C or 60°F. Add .002 to, or subtract .002 from the hydrometer readings for each 3°C or 5°F rise or fall from that temperature.

All six cells should read approximately the same. If one cell differs radically from the rest it may be due to an internal fault or possibly there has been spilling or leakage of the electrolyte. If it has been spilled, add more with the same Specific Gravity. This can be made by adding sulphuric acid to distilled water. It is highly dangerous to add water to acid.

If the battery is in a low state of charge, take the car for a long daylight run or put it on a charger at 4 amps until it gasses freely, taking out the vent plugs and refraining from using a naked light when it is gassing.

If the battery is unused for long periods, give a freshening-up charge every month. Never leave it in a discharged condition.

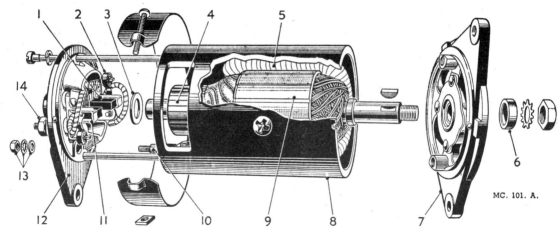

Fig 11:1   The A30 generator exploded

Key to Fig 11:1   1 Brush.   2 Brush spring.   3 Thrust collar.   4 Commutator.   5 Field coil.   6 Distance collar.
7 Driving end bracket.   8 Yoke.   9 Armature.   10 Field terminal.   11 Brush holder.   12 Commutator end bracket.
13 Field terminal nut and washers.   14 Terminal.

The generator

The A30 generator is shown exploded in **FIG 11:1**. This is a two-brush type with 'windows' in the yoke. These are covered by a band which can be unclamped to give access to the brushgear. There is a plain bearing at the commutator end and a ball bearing at the driving end.

For all practical purposes the other models are covered by **FIG 11:2**. This shows that the yoke is without 'windows' so that the end cover must be removed to get at the brushes. Again there is a plain bearing 3 at the commutator end and a ball bearing 9 at the driving end. Differences lie in the extended armature shaft of the 'Sprite' I generator to provide a tachometer drive, and the substitution of the Lucar 'tag' type connector for the field terminal post 13 on later models.

Lubrication

Every 12,000 miles unscrew the lubricator from the rear end of the generator, lift out the felt pad and spring and half fill the cap with high melting point grease. This lubricator will be found on early models only. On later cars there is a central hole in the rear end bearing. Squirt two or three drops of S.A.E.20 oil into the hole at regular intervals. The front ball bearing is packed with grease on assembly.

Checking generator output

First make sure that there is no belt slip. Adjust according to the instructions in the Cooling section.

1 Check the connections. Terminals D and F on the generator go to their respective terminals D and F on the control box, **FIG 11:6**.
2 Switch off lights and accessories. Disconnect cable from generator terminals D and F and then join the two terminals with a short piece of wire.
3 Clip the negative lead of a 20-volt moving coil voltmeter to one generator terminal and the other to a good earth on the generator body.

4 Start the engine at idling speed and gradually increase speed. The voltmeter reading should rise rapidly without fluctuations. Do not allow the reading to reach 20 volts and do not race the engine in an attempt to increase the reading. A fast idling speed should be sufficient.
5 If there is no reading check the brush gear.
6 If the reading is about $\frac{1}{2}$ to 1 volt the field winding may be faulty.
7 If it is about 4 to 5 volts the armature windings may be faulty.
8 If all is well, restore the original cable connections but leave the temporary wire in place and connect the voltmeter between the disconnected lead to the D terminal on the control box and a good earth. Run the engine as before. The reading should be the same as that recorded on the generator. No reading indicates a broken cable connection. Repeat the process, connecting the meter between the disconnected F lead at the control box and to earth.
9 If the readings are correct remove the temporary wire link. There may still be no charging current showing, however, and the control box must be tested. The procedure is covered in a later section.

Dismantling generator

1 Remove the generator by releasing the three nuts and bolts shown in **FIG 4:2** in the chapter on Cooling. If the ignition coil is mounted on the generator, detach the coil leads too.
2 Remove the spindle nut and draw off the pulley, prising the Woodruff key 8 out of the keyway.
3 Where applicable, remove the nut and washers from the field terminal post 13. Then unscrew the two long through bolts and lift off the commutator end bracket 12. The armature can now be withdrawn from the other end, coming away with end bracket 17. There is no need to remove this end bracket unless the bearing 9

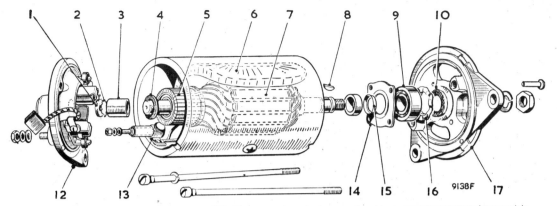

Fig 11:2   The generator on all cars except A30. The screwed terminals are replaced by Lucar connectors on later models

Key to Fig 11:2   1 Felt pad.   2 Aluminium disc.   3 Bronze bush.   4 Fibre washer.   5 Commutator.   6 Field coils.
7 Armature.   8 Shaft key.   9 Bearing.   10 Felt washer.   12 Commutator end bracket.   13 Field terminal post.
14 Bearing retaining plate.   15 Cup washer.   16 Corrugated washer.   17 Driving end bracket.

is worn. To replace the bearing, press out the armature shaft and unrivet the retaining plate 14.

SERVICING GENERATOR

Brushes

1 Pull the brushes halfway out of the brush boxes and hold them there by letting the springs press on the brush sides. Replace the commutator end bracket on the armature. Release the brushes on to the commutator and pull them up and down by the flexible leads. The brushes should be quite free. If sluggish, remove, and ease the sides by rubbing on a smooth file.
2 Replace brushes which are worn down to $\frac{11}{32}$ in on the C39 generator and $\frac{1}{4}$ in on the C40/1 type. Bed new brushes by fitting them and sliding a strip of fine glasspaper round the commutator and under the brushes, then working to and fro. Always replace brushes in their own boxes and facing the way they did before removal.

Commutator

1 Clean with a cloth moistened in petrol. If ineffective, polish by rotating the armature and using a fine glasspaper. Do not file, or use emery paper. Grains of emery may become embedded in the copper.
2 Given the use of a lathe the commutator can be skimmed to remove traces of wear, pitting or burning. Remove the minimum of copper, using a very keen tool and finally polish with fine glasspaper.
3 After skimming, the commutator insulation must be undercut as in **FIG 11:3**. Use a piece of hacksaw blade ground on the sides until it is the thickness of the mica. Undercut to a depth of $\frac{1}{32}$ in.
4 Burnt commutator segments are a sign of broken armature wires. Short-circuited windings cause darkening of the over-heated coils and badly burnt commutator segments.

Field coils

These are tested in the following way.
1 Connect a 12-volt battery between the field terminal 13

and the generator body, putting an ammeter in series. The reading should be about 2 amps. If the reading is much more it shows that field coil insulation has broken down. No reading indicates a break in the wiring of the coils.

Armature

This can only be thoroughly tested with suitable equipment not normally available to the average owner. It can be tested by substitution, however. Do not attempt to straighten a bent shaft or to machine the armature core. Replacement of worn bearings is best left to an agent. The porous bronze bush 3 must not be reamed after fitting, so that a special pilot is needed when pressing it home.

Reassembling

Proceed in the reverse sequence, lifting the brushes in their holders before fitting the commutator end cover and after replacing the armature. When the cover is within $\frac{1}{2}$ in of the generator body, the brushes can be released on to the commutator by using a small screwdriver. Make sure that the springs are pressing on the brushes properly.

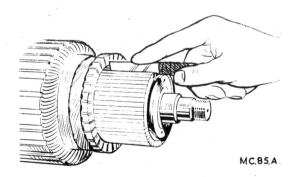

M.C.85.A.

Fig 11:3   Undercutting mica between commutator segments

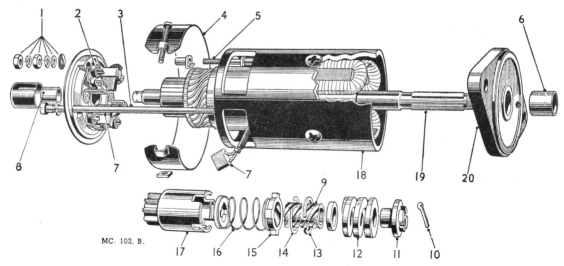

Fig 11:4   The starter motor exploded. The drive is shown in the lower section

Key to Fig 11:4 1 Terminal nuts and washers.   2 Brush spring.   3 Through bolt.   4 Cover band.   5 Terminal post.
6 Bearing bush.   7 Brushes.   8 Bearing bush.   9 Sleeve.   10 Split pin.   11 Shaft nut.   12 Main spring.
13 Retaining ring.   14 Corrugated washer.   15 Control nut.   16 Restraining spring.   17 Pinion and barrel.   18 Yoke.
19 Armature shaft.   20 Driving end bracket.

The starter

This is shown exploded in **FIG 11:4,** the pinion assembly being drawn as if pulled off from the right-hand end of the armature shaft 19.

Testing

If the starter will not operate, first make sure that the battery is well-charged. If the lights go dim when the starter control is pulled, but there is no sound from the starter, it may be jammed. Turn the squared end of the starter armature shaft as shown in **FIG 11:5.** If it is tight at first and then comes free it shows that the pinion has been released from the engine starter ring. Another method is to engage bottom gear and rock the car gently to and fro. This will often release a jammed pinion.

If the lights remain bright when the starter switch is pulled, check the switch and all the cable connections, particularly the battery terminals and those on the switch and starter. If the starter still refuses to turn it must be removed for examination.

Removing

1 Remove the distributor as described in the Ignition chapter.
2 Release the cable from the starter and unscrew the top bolt in the flange.
3 From below, release the dirt deflector under the starter and unscrew the bottom fixing bolt. Then pull the starter forward and clear of the engine.

Examination

1 Remove cover band 4 and test the freedom of the brushes in their holders. Ease in the manner described

for the generator brushes, and replace those which are worn so short that they do not bear on the commutator.
2 Clean the commutator with a petrol-moistened cloth while rotating the armature.
3 Hold the starter body in a vice and connect it to a 12-volt battery using heavy-gauge cables to carry the current required. One cable goes to the starter terminal and the other to the starter body. The starter should now run at high speed. If it does not, it must be dismantled.

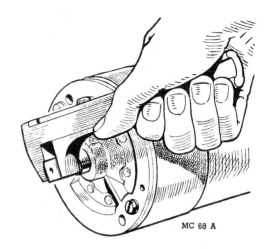

Fig 11:5   The squared end of the starter shaft can be turned to free a jammed drive

Dismantling

1 Hold back the brush springs with a wire hook and take out the brushes.
2 Remove the terminal nuts and washers 1.
3 Unscrew the through-bolts 3 and pull off the commutator end bracket.
4 Remove the driving end bracket complete with armature and drive.

SERVICING STARTER

Brushes

To renew worn brushes, unsolder the flexible leads one at a time, solder a new one in place and slip each brush in turn into its correct holder so that there is no doubt about the right position. There is no need to bed-in starter brushes.

Pinion drive

Wash the pinion and screwed sleeve in petrol and dry thoroughly. The pinion should be quite free when dry, and it must never be lubricated. If the starter spins but the pinion will not engage it is generally due to grit on the pinion and sleeve. If the parts are not oily there is less likelihood of grit sticking to them.

Dismantling drive

1 Remove split pin 10 and unscrew nut 11. On later cars, compress the spring and extract the circlip.
2 Remove the drive parts and unscrew pinion sleeve 9. If the sleeve is worn it must be replaced as a pair with the control nut 15. Renew broken springs and any badly worn parts. The barrel assembly 17 is further dismantled by removing the retaining ring 13.

The commutator

This is reconditioned in the same way as that used for the generator commutator.
Note: The mica insulation between the copper segments must not be undercut.

Field coils

The test for an open circuit is made using a 12-volt battery with a bulb in one lead. Connect one lead to the terminal post 5 and the other to the tapping point where two of the brushes are connected to the field coils. If the bulb does not light there is a break in the field coil wiring.

If the bulb lights it is still possible that there is a breakdown to earth in the coils. Check this by removing the lead from the field coil tapping point and holding it on a clean part of the starter body. If the bulb still lights it means that the field coils are earthed.

Armature

A likely cause of damage to the armature is the use of the starter control when the engine is running. This may lead to lifting of the conductors from the commutator due to excessive speed. It may also bend the armature shaft. Do not attempt to straighten a shaft nor to machine the armature core.

Bearings

These are of porous bronze and renewing them is a job which should be left to the Service agents, as they must not be reamed after fitting.

Reassemble the starter in the reverse order, lifting the brush springs with a wire hook to replace the brushes.

Control box

FIG 11:6 shows a typical control box with the cover removed. On later models the screws 1 and 2 have springs instead of locknuts; and terminal tags along the bottom instead of posts with screws. The regulator is on the left and the cut-out on the right.

The regulator controls the generator output in accordance with the load on the battery and its state of charge. The cut-out is an automatic switch for connecting or disconnecting the battery and the generator. Disconnection is necessary because the battery would otherwise discharge through a generator which was stationary or running slowly.

Adjustment—regulator electrical setting

Normally it should not be necessary to alter the regulator setting but if the generator output is not enough, or does not fall when the battery is fully charged, the setting can be checked and altered.

It is important to check first that the low state of charge in a battery is not due to a defect in it, or to a slipping belt.

1 Withdraw the cables from the terminals marked A and A1 on the control box and join them together. Connect the negative lead of a 20-volt moving coil voltmeter to the D terminal on the generator. The other meter lead goes to a good earth.
2 Slowly speed-up the engine until the meter needle 'flicks' and steadies at a reading within the limits given in Technical Data for the appropriate temperature of the regulator. If the reading steadies outside these limits the regulator must be adjusted.
3 Stop the engine and turn the adjusting screw 1 in **FIG 11:6** in a clockwise direction to raise the setting and anti-clockwise to lower it. Do this a fraction of a turn at a time.

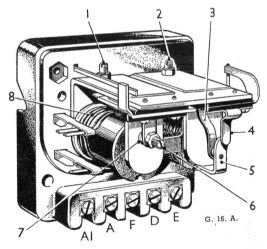

Fig 11:6 The regulator and cut-out control box. Later boxes have Lucar connectors instead of terminal posts

Key to Fig 11:6 1 Regulator adjusting screw. 2 Cut-out adjusting screw. 3 Fixed contact blade. 4 Stop arm. 5 Armature tongue and moving contact. 6 Regulator fixed contact screw. 7 Regulator moving contact. 8 Regulator series windings.

4 After each adjustment, test by running the engine at no more than half throttle. High speeds will produce a high voltage and false readings. These electrical settings must be made as quickly as possible as the rapid temperature rise in the coils will affect the meter readings.

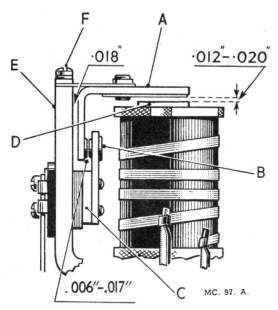

Fig 11:7 Mechanical setting of the A30 regulator

Key to Fig 11:7 A Armature. B Fixed contact. C Packing shims. D Bobbin core. E Regulator frame. F Armature fixing screws.

Mechanical setting—regulator
A30: Refer to Fig 11:7

1 Slacken the two armature fixing screws F and insert a .018-in feeler gauge between the back of the armature A and the regulator frame E.
2 Press the armature back against the frame and down on to the bobbin core D. Keep the gauge in position and lock screws F. Remove the feeler gauge.
3 Check the gap between the armature and the bobbin core. It should be within .012 to .020 in. If outside these limits add or remove shims C from behind the fixed contact.
4 Remove the gauge and press down the armature. The gap between the contacts should lie between .006 and .017 in.

All other models: Refer to Fig 11:8

If the mechanical setting has been altered or the armature removed, the regulator must be reset.
1 Slacken the fixed contact nut and unscrew the contact 3 until it is well clear of the armature contact. Slacken the armature securing screws 2.
2 Slacken the voltage adjusting screw 6 until it is well clear of the armature tension spring 1.
3 Insert a .015-in feeler gauge between the armature 4 and the core face with shim 5. Be careful not to damage

the edge of the shim. Press the armature firmly down against the gauge and tighten the screws 2.
4 Keeping the gauge in position, screw in the adjustable contact 5 until it just touches the armature contact. Tighten the locknut and remove the gauge.
5 Lastly, reset the voltage adjusting screw 2 by following the instructions given for adjusting the electrical setting.

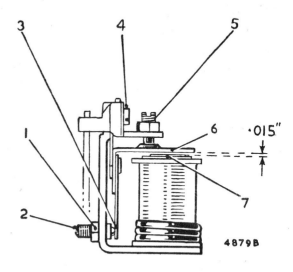

Fig 11:8 Mechanical setting of the regulator on all cars except A30

Key to Fig 11:8 1 Locknut. 2 Voltage adjusting screw. 3 Armature tension spring. 4 Armature securing screws. 5 Fixed contact adjustment screw. 6 Armature. 7 Core face and shim.

Cleaning regulator contacts

Use a fine carborundum stone or fine emery cloth. Afterwards, wipe away all traces of dust, using a non-fluffy cloth moistened with methylated spirit.

Cut-out electrical setting

If the regulator is correctly set but the battery is still not being charged, the cut-out may need adjusting. Check the voltage at which the cut-out operates as follows.
1 Connect a voltmeter between the terminals D and E on the control box.
2 Start the engine and slowly increase the speed until the cut-out points are seen to close. This should happen between 12.7 and 13.3 volts.
3 If outside these limits, turn the adjusting screw 2 in FIG 11:6, first undoing the locknut if one is fitted. Turn the screw in a clockwise direction to raise the voltage setting, and anti-clockwise to reduce it. Turn a fraction at a time and test after each adjustment. Like the regulator, electrical settings must be made very quickly or the rapid rise in coil temperature will affect the meter readings.
4 Adjustment of the 'drop off' voltage is done by carefully bending the fixed contact blade. This point is covered in the next section.
If the cut-out does not operate there may be a break in

the wiring of the regulator and cut-out unit. Testing will entail the removal of the control box. The circuit diagram is shown by **FIG 11:9.**

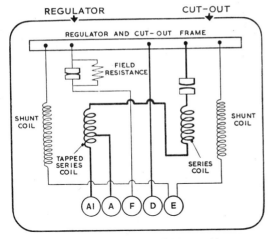

Fig 11:9   Circuit diagram of the control box

Cut-out mechanical setting

A30: Refer to Fig 11:10

1 Slacken the two armature fixing screws D and the fixed contact screws F.
2 Insert a .008-in feeler gauge between the back of the armature B and the cut-out frame G. Put a .011 to .015-in feeler between the underside of the armature shim C and the core face A. Press the armature down and back against the two feelers and tighten screws D.
3 With the feeler gauges still in place, set the gap between the armature and the stop plate arm H to .030 to .034 in by carefully bending the arm.
4 Remove the gauges and tighten screws F. Then insert a .025-in feeler gauge between the core face and the armature. Press the armature down and measure the gap between the contacts at E. This should be .002 to .006 in. Adjust this gap by adding or removing shims beneath the fixed contact plate.

All other models: Refer to Fig 11:11

If the setting of the cut-out armature has been disturbed, the correct settings can be made as follows:
1 Slacken the locknut if fitted and unscrew the adjusting screw until it is well clear of the armature tension spring. Slacken the two armature securing screws.
2 Press the armature firmly down against the copper-sprayed core face and retighten the armature securing screws.
3 Using a pair of round-nosed pliers .adjust the gap between the armature stop arm and the armature tongue by bending the arm. The gap should lie between .025 and .040 in with the armature pressed squarely down on the core face.
4 In the same way the insulated fixed contact blade must be bent so that there is a 'follow-through' or deflection of the contact of .010 to .020 in.
Finally, reset the cut-out adjusting screw according to the instructions for cut-out electrical setting.

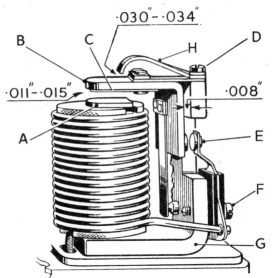

Fig 11:10   Mechanical setting of the A30 cut-out

Key to Fig 11:10   A Bobbin core.   B Armature.   C .005 in brass shim.   D Armature fixing screws.   E Fixed contact. F Fixed contact screws.   G Cut-out frame.

Note: Do not use emery cloth or carborundum stone for cleaning cut-out points, which are soft. If the contacts are dirty, rough or burnt, place a strip of fine glasspaper between them and draw it through, holding the contacts together. Do this two or three times then reverse the paper to clean the second contact. Use a non-fluffy cloth moistened in methylated spirit to clean away all dust.

Fuses

The open-type fuse unit carries two 35-amp cartridge fuses held in spring clips. The fuse between terminal blocks A1 and A2 is to protect the general auxiliary circuits which are independent of the ignition switch, e.g. the horn. The other fuse between blocks A3 and A4 protects the ignition circuit and those auxiliaries which operate only when the ignition is switched on, e.g. fuel gauge, wiper motor and flashers.

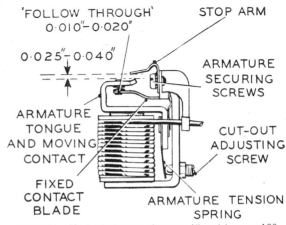

Fig 11:11   Mechanical setting of cut-out. All models except A30

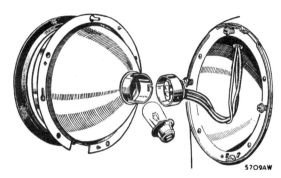

Fig 11:12 The headlamp unit showing the pre-focus bulb and three adjusting screws

HEADLAMPS

With pre-focus bulbs, refer to Fig 11:12

If the lamp is already correctly focused, no adjustment is required when a new bulb is fitted. To reach the bulb, remove the bezel if fitted.

1 Remove the rim screw and lift the bottom of the rim outwards to release it.
2 Remove the dust-excluding rubber. Three spring-loaded screws will now be seen. Press in the light unit against the springs and turn it anti-clockwise until the screw heads can be disengaged. Do not disturb the screws as they adjust the beam setting. Remove the bayonet cap at the back of the reflector and remove the bulb. Locate the replacement bulb correctly.
3 When replacing the parts make sure that the dust-excluding rubber has its thick inner edge resting in the recess in the light unit rim.

Beam setting

The three screws which accept the keyhole slots of the light unit are the means of adjusting it for beam setting. Turn the top one for vertical setting and one or both of the others for horizontal setting.

Sealed-beam headlamps

After removing the rim, an inner rim will be seen. Take out its three securing screws and pull out the light unit. Pull off the three-pin socket from the back. The vertical beam-setting screw will be found at the top, and there is a single screw on the right-hand side for horizontal adjustment.

Windscreen wipers

The motor and drive assembly is shown in **FIG 11:13**. Note that the reciprocating rack 13 slides in the outer casing 11, engaging the gear on spindle 16 to produce the necessary arc of wiper movement. To remove the motor, disconnect the outer casing from the motor gearbox by unscrewing the union nut. Take off the wiper blades, remove the motor mounting nuts and washers and pull the motor away, bringing the inner rack 13 with it. To inspect the commutator and brush gear, remove the cover from the end opposite to the gearbox. Clean the commutator with a petrol-moistened cloth and examine the brush gear. The spring must have sufficient tension to keep the brushes in good contact, and the brush levers must be free. If the brush assembly is removed, mark it to ensure

that it is replaced as before. Lubricate the bearings sparingly with S.A.E. 20 oil. Grease is used in the gearbox, on the cable rack and in the wheelboxes.

Wiper parking

The self-parking position can be adjusted by altering the limit switch 7. Slacken the four securing screws on the gearbox cover and note the projection near the rim of the limit switch. Position the projection in line with the groove in the gearbox cover. Turn the limit switch 25 degs in an anti-clockwise direction and tighten the cover screws. If the wiping blades are required to park on the opposite side of the screen, turn the switch back 180 degs in a clockwise direction. Do not attempt to turn the switch through a full circle.

Fuel gauge

If the gauge registers nothing or is incorrect, check that current is reaching the B terminal on the gauge. If current is there, proceed as follows:

1 Disconnect the green with black cable from the T terminal on the gauge. If it does not register 'FULL' with the ignition switched on, the gauge is faulty.
2 If the gauge seems correct, leave the cable still disconnected and connect a temporary cable from terminal T to earth. If the gauge does not register 'EMPTY' with the ignition switched on, then the gauge is faulty.
3 If the gauge still seems to be sound, disconnect the green with black cable from the fuel tank unit, and then connect a temporary cable from the fuel gauge terminal T to the tank unit terminal. If the gauge does not register according to the contents of the tank, or registers 'FULL' irrespective of it, then the tank unit is at fault. The ignition must be switched on during this test. If the contents of the tank are registered correctly when the temporary cable is connected, but 'EMPTY' when reverting to the normal wiring, then the cable between the gauge and the tank unit is earthed.

IMPORTANT

Do not connect the battery directly to the terminal of the tank unit.

Flasher units

These cannot be dismantled for subsequent reassembly. A defective unit must be renewed, taking care to follow the original connections.

Checking faulty operation

1 Check the bulbs for broken filaments.
2 Use the wiring diagram in Technical Data to check the connections.
3 Check the appropriate fuse.
4 Switch on the ignition and check with a voltmeter that there is battery voltage between the flasher unit terminal B (or +) and earth.
5 Connect together flasher unit terminals B (or +) and L. Operate the direction indicator switch. If the flasher bulbs now light the unit is defective and must be renewed.

Before fitting a new flasher unit or installing a flashing light system, test the circuits. Join together the cables normally connected to the unit terminals. These are green, green with brown and light green. Operate the indicator switch and if a wrong connection has been made the ignition auxiliaries fuse will blow but there will be no damage to the flasher unit.

FAULT DIAGNOSIS

(a) Battery discharged

1 Terminals loose or dirty
2 Lighting circuit shorted
3 Generator not charging
4 Regulator or cut-out units not working properly
5 Battery internally defective

(b) Insufficient charging current

1 Loose or corroded battery terminals
2 Generator belt slipping

(c) Battery will not hold charge

1 Low electrolyte level
2 Battery plates sulphated
3 Electrolyte leakage from cracked cell or top sealing compound
4 Plate separators ineffective

(d) Battery overcharged

1 Voltage regulator needs adjusting

(e) Generator output low or nil

1 Belt broken or slipping
2 Regulator unit out of adjustment
3 Worn bearings. Loose pole pieces
4 Commutator worn, burned or shorted

5 Armature shaft bent or worn
6 Insulation proud between commutator segments
7 Brushes sticking, springs weak or broken
8 Field coil wires shorted, broken or burned

(f) Starter motor lacks power or will not operate

1 Battery discharged, loose cable connections
2 Starter pinion jammed in mesh with flywheel gear
3 Starter switch faulty
4 Brushes worn or sticking, leads detached or shorting
5 Commutator dirty or worn
6 Starter shaft bent
7 Engine abnormally stiff

(g) Starter motor runs but does not turn engine

1 Pinion sticking on screwed sleeve
2 Broken teeth on pinion or flywheel gears

(h) Noisy starter pinion when engine is running

1 Restraining spring weak or broken

(j) Starter motor inoperative

1 Battery discharged, loose cable connections
2 Armature or field coils faulty
3 Brushes worn or stuck

(k) Starter motor rough or noisy

1 Mounting bolts loose
2 Damaged pinion or flywheel gear teeth
3 Main pinion spring broken

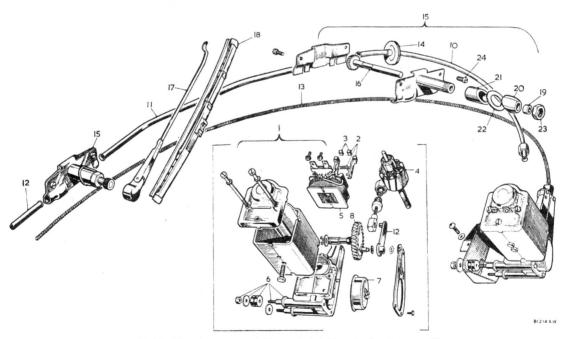

Fig 11:13   The wiper motor and drive exploded. Mounting brackets may differ

Key to Fig 11:13   1 Windshield wiper motor.   2 Brush gear.   3 Brush.   4 Armature.   5 Field coil.   6 Fixing parts.
7 Parking switch.   8 Gear and shaft.   10 Motor to wheelbox outer casing.   11 Wheelbox to wheelbox outer casing.
12 Wheelbox extension outer casing.   13 Cross-head and rack assembly.   14 Grommet.   15 Wheelbox.   16 Spindle and gear.
17 Arm.   18 Blade.

(l) Lamps inoperative or erratic

1 Battery low, bulbs burned out
2 Faulty earthing of lamps or battery
3 Lighting switch faulty. Loose or broken wiring connections

(m) Wiper motor sluggish, taking high current

1 Faulty armature
2 Bearings out of alignment
3 Commutator dirty or short-circuited
4 Wheelbox spindle binding, cable rack tight in housing

(n) Wiper motor operates but does not drive arms

1 Wheelbox gear and spindle worn
2 Cable rack faulty
3 Gearbox components worn

(o) Fuel gauge does not register

1 No battery supply to gauge
2 Gauge casing not earthed
3 Cable between gauge and tank unit earthed

(p) Fuel gauge registers 'FULL'

1 Cable between gauge and tank unit broken or disconnected

CHAPTER 12

BODYWORK

Body finishing   Door locks   Hinges   Removing glass   Window regulators
Fitting windscreens   Removing instrument panels   Removing fascias

Bodywork

It is almost inevitable that the bodywork of the older car will suffer from some minor damage at least. This can be repaired by the operator who knows that a perfect finish can only be obtained by initial care in levelling up and rubbing down. Spray painting is the best method of matching new paintwork with old, and it is a good idea to leave large areas to the expert. This also applies to the repair of severe damage to sheet metalwork, where the specialised technique of panel beating is not usually within the powers of the amateur.

It is tempting to knock out small dents with a hammer, but too much beating may result in 'oil-canning' or popping in and out. Further hammering will only make matters worse. It is a better plan to fill such dents.

If a filler such as primer surfacer or a paste stopper is used, it is essential to remove any wax polish from the original finish by means of a solvent such as white spirit. When the filler is dry, rub it down with 400 grade 'Wet or Dry' paper until the surface is smooth and flush with the surrounding area. Apply the retouching paint by spray, keeping it wet in the centre and light and dry round the edges. After a few hours of drying time, use a cutting compound to remove the dry spray and finish with liquid polish. Colour-matching old and new paint is difficult, so spray a complete wing rather than a small patch. The following sections deal with the dismantling and adjustment of the mechanical parts of the bodywork.

Doors—A30 and A35

To remove the door trim refer to **FIG 12:1.** Lift the trim progressively free, using a screwdriver or the special tool depicted. Refit by holding the trim in place and then peel the rubber lip over the edge.

On later cars, take off the pull strap and inner door handle first. The trim is then prised away using a screwdriver as shown in **FIG 12:4.** Pull the top away first and then lift the trim out of the bottom channel.

Locks

Prise the private lock from outside, at the same time depressing the spring clips inside the door. When refitting it is important to turn the square socket clockwise as far as it will go. With a rubber washer behind the lockplate, the lock can be pushed in until the clips spring into place.

Removing

Remove the escutcheon plate and knob from the remote control lever. Extract the four screws from the remote control, the four screws from the bolt plate and withdraw the assembly. Old and new locks are shown in **FIG 12:2.**

Hinges

If it is necessary to remove all the hinge screws, be careful that the hinges do not drop down inside the body. When replacing hinges do not fully tighten the screws until the door hangs and fits properly.

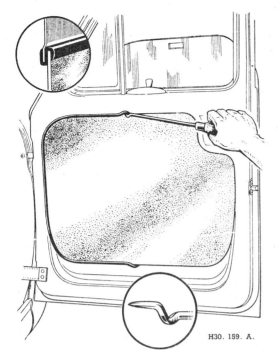

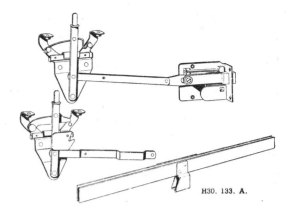

Fig 12:2 Door locks on A30 and A35. Early type (top) and later type (below), with glass channel

Fig 12:1 Fitting an A30 trim panel with the tool shown in the inset

Removing front windows

1 Take away the door trim and the window arm shown in **FIG 12:3**. A small hole at the end of the arm carries a steel ball.

2 Remove the guide channels from the door frame by unscrewing the five fixing screws from the side and top. Free the channels from the fixing brackets at the lower end.

3 Work the glass out from below and the rear channel from above, then remove the other channel.

Replace by reversing the procedure but adjust the channels at their lower ends until the glass slides smoothly. With the remote control lever in the locking position the glass stop channel must engage with the stop bracket on the lever. On early cars the window should open one inch before engaging the stop bracket. Releasing the lock should allow the window to open fully under slight pressure. When fully open the arm should rest on the rubber stop. On later cars the remote control will lock the front glasses in the fully closed or partially opened position, see **FIG 12:2**.

Front and rear louvres—removing

1 Withdraw the three securing screws inside the sealing rubber.

2 Close the louvre and support the inside of the glass with the hand. Strike the upper outside surface of the glass sharply with the other hand so that the top of the assembly will be forced free, and lift away.

Optional rear quarter lights—removing

1 Open the window and release the catch from the door shell.

2 Open the hinge to its fullest extent and remove the four screws revealed. Lift away the window.

Rear door windows—removing

1 Support on the inside and strike smartly with the flat of the hand on the outside at the top. When the top is released, the glass and weatherstrip can be lifted out from the inside.

Refit the glass by using the cord method described later for fitting windscreens.

Doors: A40

To lock the door and the window glass, the door must first be closed. Do not attempt to force the handle into the locked position while the door is open. To remove the door trim set the interior handle to the 'normal' position

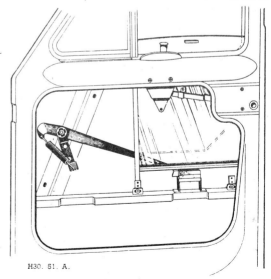

Fig 12:3 Window lift and remote control on A30

with the window unlocked, and then remove the handle. Prise the trim panel away with a screwdriver to release the spring clips as in **FIG 12:4**. When replacing, locate the loose end of the plastic cover inside the lower aperture in the door.

Locks

To remove the locks refer to **FIG 12:5**.

1 Remove screws C and D, the door pull at E and screw F.
2 Release the remote control link by removing circlip and washer G.
3 Take out the remote control screws H, press the loose end of the front window channel out of the way and remove the control.
4 Take out screws I and J. Pull the rear window channel away from the lock and turn it so that the lock can be manoeuvred round it and the outside push button passed through. Do not use force. The lock is then passed down until it is clear of the window channel and can be drawn out through the lower aperture.

To replace the locks refer to **FIG 12:6**.

1 Grease all moving parts, but never the private lock cylinder with anything but oil. Insert the lock and fixing screws. Move the latch downwards into the closed position L.
2 The remote control is supplied with a peg M to hold it in the locked position and must be fitted like this. Insert through the upper aperture connecting link first. Fit the three securing screws but do not tighten.
3 Replace the link on the lock lever stud and fit the washer and circlip G (**FIG 12:5**). To align the lock assembly, slide the remote control towards the lock.

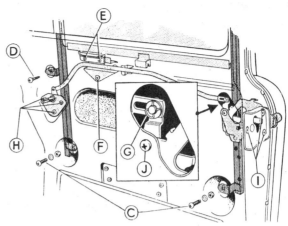

Fig 12:5   Lock and remote control mechanism on A40

The slotted end of the link and the stop on the lock lever will then be in position N. Tighten the remote control screws and remove the temporary peg. Replace all the other parts.

The striker unit is fixed by screws K in **FIG 12:6**. These screw into an adjustable tapping plate inside the door pillar. Do not disturb the setting unless adjustment is needed or a new assembly is to be fitted. To do this:

1 Attach the striker unit loosely, then move it to a position which seems suitable and tighten the screws.
2 Proceed to adjust the position until the door closes easily without rattling and does not lift or drop during closing.

The striker must be kept in a horizontal plane relative to the door axis during these adjustments. Finally, lubricate with oil.

Front ventilator removal

1 Remove the inside door handle and the trim pad. Remove the window glass stop from the door, hold the regulator against the spring pressure and lower the glass as far as possible. Tie the regulator down.
2 Slide the clip along the top of the window moulding to expose the join and carefully prise the moulding away.
3 Remove the ventilator securing screws from the upper and lower front corners and those holding the window channel in position. Slide the channel downwards and remove the ventilator as the top of the frame is pulled gently rearwards and upwards. Reassemble in the reverse order.

Front ventilator adjustment

The lower hinge pin of the ventilator carries a spring and two locknuts. To increase the friction unlock the nuts and screw upwards, locking them again when the ventilator remains in any required position. Conversely, slacken the nuts to reduce friction.

Window regulator—A40, II

The attachment screws are shown in **FIG 12:7**. To remove the mechanism:

1 Detach the interior door handle from shank 1. Press the regulator handle collar inwards against spring pressure

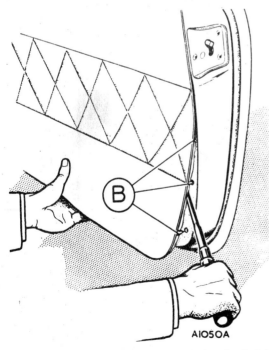

Fig 12:4   Removing an A40 trim panel. Spring clips lock in holes B

to reveal the peg shown in **FIG 12:8** which can then be pushed out to release the handle.

2 Remove the door trim panel and plastic moisture deflector.

3 Remove screw 4, wind down the window about four inches and wedge it.

4 Remove the four screws 3 and lift the regulating arm out of its lifting channel.

5 Press the glass frame away from the door panel to allow the regulating mechanism and arm to be removed through the space at the bottom. Remove the three screws to detach the glass stop.

Replace in the reverse order. The plastic moisture deflector goes behind the door trim pad.

Doors—'Sprites' I, II and III. 'Midgets' I and II

FIG 12:9 shows the hinge fixings. To remove a door first detach the inner end of the check strap from the door pillar.

The door catch and operating handle can be taken out complete by removing the four screws inside the door. On 'Sprite' III and 'Midget' II the remote control can also be released from the inner door panel. With the trim pad removed, unscrew the nut and drive screw from the outer door handle and lift off the handle. The window regulator handle is removed by pressing the handle finisher inwards until the cross-pin can be pushed out.

Window regulators—'Sprite' III and 'Midget' II

These can be removed by referring to **FIG 12:10**.

1 Take off the door pull, the inner door handle and the window regulating handle. Lever away the trim panel with a screwdriver.

2 Remove the regulator securing screws 4 and screws 5.

3 Release the window regulator arm from the bottom of the window glass. Lift up the glass clear of the regulator and remove the regulator and bracket assembly. Reverse the procedure to replace.

Ventilators—'Sprite' III and 'Midget' II

To remove these refer to **FIG 12:10**.

1 Remove the trim panel, door handles and window regulator handle.

2 Remove the set screws and nuts holding the ventilator top to the door.

3 Remove steady set screw 3 and lower securing screws 2. This will release the front door glass channel.

4 Remove the channel and the door glass stop and lift out the ventilator assembly. Refit by reversing the procedure.

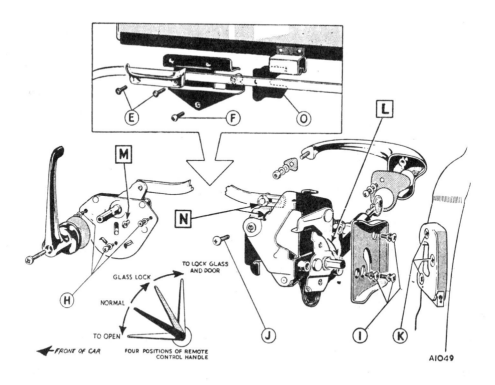

Fig 12:6   A40 lock and remote control exploded

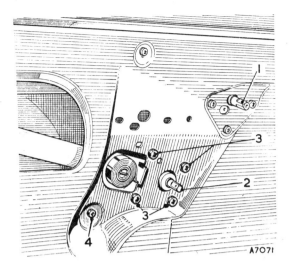

Fig 12:7 Window regulating mechanism on A40 II

Door glass—'Sprite' III and 'Midget' II

1 Proceed as for removing the ventilator but also take out the drive screws securing the backing panel to the door. Remove the inner door cappings and set screws 6.
2 Remove the glass stop in the bottom of the door.
3 Remove the regulator screws 4 and the extension screws 5.
4 Lower the door glass and remove the ventilator assembly. Lift out the door glass. To refit reverse the removal procedure.

Fitting windscreens

It can be a puzzling problem to fit the rubber weatherstrip round a windscreen into the body aperture. This can be solved by using cords to peel the rubber lips over the steel flanges, as shown by **FIG 12:11**. The rubber stripping is first fitted to the glass and then cords are placed in

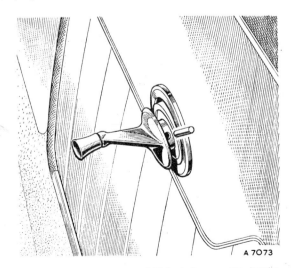

Fig 12:8 Locating peg on A40 II window regulator handle

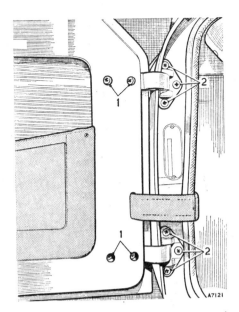

Fig 12:9 'Sprite' and MG door hinge fixings

the two grooves, or a single cord in the case of the backlight or rear window. An easy way to lay the cord is to insert the first six inches and feed the rest in using a short piece of small-bore tubing. The cord passes through the tube, the inner end of which is laid in the groove and drawn round. Start and finish at the same place, leaving generous lengths of the two cord ends to give good handholds. Press the glass into place and draw the cord out of the groove. This will peel the rubber lip over the body flange.

The last operation will be to make a watertight seal between the lips and the glass, or the lips and steel flange. Preferably using a nozzle, squeeze Seelastik well down into the groove so that there will be a surplus to be pressed out when the lip returns to normal.

Instrument panel—A30

The panel is held in place by four recessed-head screws and four spire nuts behind the panel. The instruments and electrical connections are accessible on releasing the panel.

Later A30 and A35

Remove the instrument panel by unscrewing the two knurled nuts, one on each side of the panel behind the fascia. This releases the securing clips. The panel is drawn forward, all connections detached and the panel removed.

Removing fascia

Remove the fillets from the windscreen side pillars. Release the starter pull-cable from the switch on the bulkhead and the choke cable at the carburetter, also releasing the choke outer cable from the bulkhead. Remove the trafficator control by unscrewing two set screws and releasing three electrical cables. Release the demister pipes if a heater is fitted.

The fascia is fixed to the scuttle by two hexagon bolts at each lower corner and four recessed-head screws underneath. Remove these and lift the fascia off the four clips along the upper edge.

ing column surround. Unscrew the speedometer and tachometer drives from the instruments and the oil pressure pipe from the gauge. It is advisable to withdraw the water temperature element from its connection with the radiator. Release the choke and starter cables. The fascia can then be pulled out to give access to the backs of the instruments.

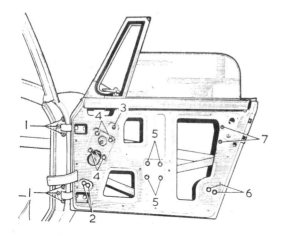

Fig 12:10   The door assembly on 'Sprite' III and 'Midget' II

Key to Fig 12:10 1 Door hinge securing set screws. 2 Ventilator securing set screws.   3 Ventilator steady set screws.   4 Regulator securing set screws.   5 Regulator extension securing set screws.   6 Rear door glass guide channel securing set screws.   7 Door lock remote control securing set screws.

Removing fascia—'Sprites' and 'Midgets'

Remove the steering wheel. In each corner at the top of the fascia is a nut and bolt, and there is a nut in the centre. Remove these together with two cross-head screws on the bottom edge and three set screws behind the steer-

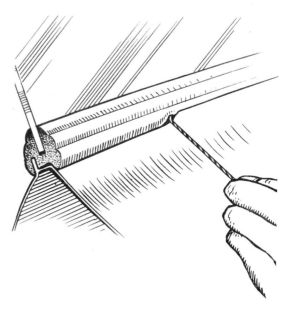

Fig 12:11   Using a cord to fit the windscreen weatherstrip to the A30 scuttle

APPENDIX

TECHNICAL DATA

Engine Details   Ignition System
Carburetter Details   Gearbox
Battery and Generator   Cooling system
Front suspension   Steering   Rear axle

WIRING DIAGRAMS

TECHNICAL DATA

ENGINE DETAILS

Dimensions are in inches unless otherwise stated

Bore and stroke (mm):
- 800 cc ... ... 58×76.2
- 948 cc ... ... 62.94×76.2
- 1098 cc ... ... 64.58×83.72

Compression ratio (low):
- 800 cc 7.2:1
- 948 cc (A35 and A40) 7.2:1
- 948 cc ('Sprite' I and II, 'Midget' I) 8.3:1
- 1098 cc (A35 and A40) 7.5:1
- 1098 cc ('Sprite' II and III, 'Midget' I and II) 8.1:1

Compression ratio (high):
- 948 cc (A35 and A40) 8.3:1
- 948 cc ('Sprite' II and 'Midget' I) 9.0:1
- 1098 cc (A40) 8.5:1
- 1098 cc ('Sprite' II and III, 'Midget' I and II) 8.9:1

Main bearings, journal diameter:
- All capacities 1.7505–1.7510

Main bearing liners, running clearance:
- 800 cc and 948 cc (A30 and A35) 0.0005–0.002
- 948 cc ('Sprites' and 'Midgets') 0.001–0.0025
- 948 cc (A40) 0.0005–0.003
- 1098 cc (A35 and A40) 0.001–0.0027
- 1098 cc ('Sprites' and 'Midgets') 0.001–0.0025

Main bearings, lining material:
- 800 and 948 cc (A30, A35, A40 and 'Sprite' I) ... ... White metal
- 948 cc ('Sprite' II and 'Midget' I) ... ... Lead–indium
- 1098 cc (A35 and A40) ... ... Copper–lead
- 1098 cc ('Sprites' and 'Midgets') ... ... Lead–indium

Crankshaft end float:
- All capacities 0.002–0.003

Crankpin diameter:
- 800 cc 1.4379–1.4384
- All other capacities 1.6254–1.6259

Connecting-rod centres:
- All capacities 5.75

Big-end bearings, running clearance:
- All capacities 0.001–0.0025

Big-end bearings, lining material:
- 800 cc (early A30) ... ... White metal
- 800 cc (later A30) ... ... Copper–lead with lead–indium or lead–tin plating
- 948 cc (A35) ... ... Copper–lead with lead–indium or lead–tin plating
- 948 cc (A40, 'Sprite' I) ... ... Copper–lead
- 948 cc ('Sprite' II, 'Midget' I) ... ... Lead–indium
- 1098 cc (A35 and A40) ... ... Copper–lead
- 1098 cc ('Sprites' and 'Midgets') ... ... Lead–indium

Connecting-rod end float on crankpin:
- 800 cc 0.006–0.010
- All other capacities 0.008–0.012

Clamped gudgeon pin:
- Diameter (800 cc and 948 cc) 0.6244–0.6246
- Clearance in piston 0.0001–0.0003

Fully floating gudgeon pin:
Fit in piston (1098 cc) ... ... Hand push
Piston type ... ... Aluminium alloy
Std. piston, suitable bore size:
800 cc 2.2807–2.2810
948 cc 2.4778–2.4781
1098 cc 2.5424–2.5447
Piston oversizes:
800 cc and 948 cc ... ... +0.010, +0.020,
+0.030 and +0.040
1098 cc ... ... +0.010 and +0.020
Piston clearance, bottom of skirt:
800 cc and 948 cc (A35) 0.0006–0.0014
948 cc (A40) 0.0006–0.0012
948 cc ('Sprite' I) 0.001–0.0016
948 cc ('Sprite' II, 'Midget' I) 0.0016–0.0022
1098 cc 0.0005–0.0011
Piston clearance, top of skirt:
948 cc ('Sprite' II and 'Midget' I) 0.0036–0.0042
1098 cc 0.0021–0.0037
Piston rings, compression:
Top ... ... Plain
Second ... ... Taper
Third ... ... Taper (early A30, plain)
Fourth piston ring, all capacities ... ... Slotted scraper
Width of compression rings:
800 cc and 948 cc 0.069–0.070
1098 cc (top ring) 0.062–0.0625
1098 cc (second and third rings) 0.0615–0.0625
Width of slotted scraper ring:
All capacities 0.124–0.125
Ring gap, fitted 0.007–0.012
Ring clearance in groove:
800 cc and 948 cc 0.0015–0.0035
1098 cc 0.002–0.004
Camshaft journal diameters:
Front 1.6655–1.666
Centre 1.62275–1.62325
Rear 1.3725–1.3735
Camshaft bearings:
Front ... ... Steel-backed white metal
Centre and rear ... ... Direct in crankcase
(All 'Sprites' and 'Midgets', except 'Sprite' I, have three white-
metalled bearing liners)
Camshaft clearance:
Front bearing 0.001–0.002
Centre and rear bearings 0.00125–0.00275
Camshaft end float 0.003–0.007
Timing chain ... ... Single roller
Timing chain, pitch 0.375
Timing chain, length ... ... 52 pitches
Valve seat angle ... ... 45 deg

Valve lift:
800 cc and 948 cc (A30, A35, A40, I and II) 0.285
948 cc ('Sprite' I) 0.285
948 cc ('Sprite' II and 'Midget' I) 0.312
1098 cc 0.312

Valve head diameter, inlet:							
800 cc (A30) ...	...	...	...	...	...	...	1.093–1.098
948 cc (A35, A40, I and II)	...	...	...	...	...	...	1.093–1.098
948 cc ('Sprite' I)	...	...	...	...	...	...	1.0937
948 cc ('Sprite' II and 'Midget' I)		...	...	...	...	...	1.151–1.156
1098 cc	...	...	...	...	...	...	1.151–1.156
Valve head diameter, exhaust:							
800 cc (A30) ...	...	...	...	...	...	...	1.000–1.005
948 cc (A35, A40, I and II)	...	...	...	...	...	...	1.000–1.005
948 cc ('Sprites' and 'Midgets')		...	...	...	...	...	1.00–1.005
1098 cc	...	...	...	...	...	...	1.00–1.005
Valve stem diameter, inlet:							
800 cc (A30) ...	...	...	...	...	...	...	0.2793–0.2798
948 cc (A35, A40, I and II)	...	...	...	...	...	...	0.2793–0.2798
948 cc ('Sprites' and 'Midgets')		...	...	...	...	...	0.2793–0.2798
1098 cc	...	...	...	...	...	...	0.2793–0.2798
Valve stem diameter, exhaust:							
800 cc (A30) ...	...	...	...	...	...	...	0.2788–0.2793
948 cc (A35, A40, I and II)	...	...	...	...	...	...	0.2788–0.2793
948 cc ('Sprites' and 'Midgets')		...	...	...	...	...	0.2788–0.2793
1098 cc	...	...	...	...	...	...	0.2788–0.2793
Valve stem clearance, inlet:							
All capacities ...	...	...	...	...	...	...	0.0015–0.0025
Valve stem clearance, exhaust:							
800 cc ...	...	...	...	...	...	...	0.001–0.002
948 cc and 1098 cc	...	...	...	...	...	...	0.002–0.003
Valve rocker clearance (cold):							
All capacities ...	...	...	...	...	...	...	0.012
Competition work ('Sprites' and 'Midgets')		...	...	...	...	...	0.015
For checking timing only:							
800 cc and 948 cc (except 'Sprite' II and 'Midget' I)		...	...	...	...	...	0.019
948 cc 'Sprite' II and 'Midget' I		...	...	...	...	...	0.021
1098 cc	...	...	...	...	...	...	0.021
Valve springs—free length:							
800 cc and 948 cc (A30, A35 and A40, I and II)		...	...	...	...	...	1.625
948 cc ('Sprite' I)	...	...	...	...	...	...	1.75
948 cc ('Sprite' II and 'Midget' I), inner		...	...	...	...	...	1.672
948 cc ('Sprite' II and 'Midget' I), outer		...	...	...	...	...	1.75
1098 cc (A35 and A40, II)		...	...	...	...	...	1.75
1098 cc ('Sprites' and 'Midgets'), inner		...	...	...	...	...	1.672
1098 cc ('Sprites' and 'Midgets'), outer		...	...	...	...	...	1.75
Valve spring pressure (valve closed):							
800 cc and 948 cc (A30, A35 and A40)		...	...	...	...	...	35.5–39.5 lb
948 cc ('Sprite' I)	...	...	...	...	...	...	52.5 lb
948 cc ('Sprite' II and 'Midget' I), inner		...	...	...	...	...	18 lb
948 cc ('Sprite' II and 'Midget' I), outer		...	...	...	...	...	52 lb
1098 cc (A35 and A40, II)		...	...	...	...	...	52.5 lb
1098 cc ('Sprites' and 'Midgets'), inner		...	...	...	...	...	18 lb
1098 cc ('Sprites' and 'Midgets'), outer		...	...	...	...	...	52 lb
Valve timing (A30 and 948 cc A35, A40 and 'Sprite' I):							
Inlet opens ...	...	...	...	...	...	...	5 deg before tdc
Inlet closes ...	...	...	...	...	...	...	45 deg after bdc
Exhaust opens ...	...	...	...	...	...	...	40 deg before bdc
Exhaust closes ...	...	...	...	...	...	...	10 deg after tdc
With rocker clearance of 0.019, for checking only							
Valve timing (948 cc 'Sprite' II and 'Midget' I. All 1098 cc):							
Inlet opens ...	...	...	...	...	...	...	5 deg before tdc
Inlet closes ...	...	...	...	...	...	...	45 deg after bdc

| Exhaust opens ... | ... | ... | ... | ... | ... | ... | 51 deg before bdc |
| Exhaust closes ... | ... | ... | ... | ... | ... | ... | 21 deg at tdc |

With rocker clearance of 0.021, for checking only

Oil sump capacity including filter (pints):

| All capacities ... | ... | ... | ... | ... | ... | 6½ |

Oil pressure (normal running), lb/sq in:

| A30 ... | ... | ... | ... | ... | ... | 50–55 |
| All others ... | ... | ... | ... | ... | ... | 60 |

Tightening torque (lb/ft). All capacities:

Cylinder head nuts ...	...	...	...	...	...	40
Main bearing cap bolts	...	...	...	...	...	60
Big-end cap bolts ...	...	...	...	...	...	35
Gudgeon pin clamp screw	...	...	...	...	...	25
Flywheel bolts ...	...	...	...	...	...	35–40
Rocker pedestal nuts ...	...	...	...	...	...	25
Sump to crankcase bolts	...	...	...	...	...	6
Rocker cover nuts ...	...	...	...	...	...	4

IGNITION SYSTEM

Spark plug type, all capacities	...	...	...	...	...	Champion N5
Spark plug gap ...	...	...	...	...	...	0.025
Contact breaker gap ...	...	...	...	...	...	0.014

Static setting, Premium fuel:

A30 ...	...	...	...	...	...	11 deg before tdc
948 cc (high comp.) A35, A40 and 'Sprite' I ...	...	...	5 deg before tdc
948 cc (high comp.) 'Sprite' II and 'Midget' I ...	...	...	4 deg before tdc
1098 cc (high comp.) 'Sprite' III and 'Midget' II	...	...	5 deg before tdc

Static setting (low comp.):

A30 (commercial fuel) ...	...	...	...	...	...	6½ deg before tdc
948 cc (A35 and A40, Commercial fuel)	...	...	...	2 deg before tdc
948 cc ('Sprite' II and 'Midget' I)	...	...	...	...	1 deg before tdc
1098 cc (A35 and A40) ...	...	...	...	...	3 deg before tdc
1098 cc ('Sprites' and 'Midgets') ...	...	...	...	3–5 deg before tdc

Stroboscope setting at 600 engine rev/min:

| 1098 cc (A40) ... | ... | ... | ... | ... | ... | 6 deg before tdc |
| 1098 cc ('Sprites' and 'Midgets') ... | ... | ... | ... | 8 deg before tdc |

Distributor type (Lucas):

A30, 948 cc A35 and A40, I ...	...	...	...	...	D.M.2
'Sprite' I ...	...	...	...	...	...	D.M.2–P.H.4
948 cc 'Sprite' II and 'Midget' I	...	...	...	...	D.M.2–P.4
1098 cc ...	...	...	...	...	...	25 D.4

Coil type (Lucas):

| Early A30 ... | ... | ... | ... | ... | ... | Q.12 |
| All other models ... | ... | ... | ... | ... | ... | L.A.12 |

CARBURETTER DETAILS

Type (early A30) ...	...	...	...	...	...	...	Zenith 26 JS
Choke ...	...	...	...	...	...	...	18
Main jet ...	...	...	...	...	...	...	95 or 113
Main air jet ...	...	...	...	...	...	...	160
Slow running jet ...	...	...	...	...	...	...	40
Slow running air bleed	...	...	...	...	...	...	80
Needle and seating	...	...	...	...	...	...	1.5 mm

| Type (A30 later, 948 cc A35 and A40, I) ... | ... | ... | ... | Zenith 26 VME |

		A30 (later)	A35	A40, I
Choke	...	20	22	22

Main jet ...	70	80	80
Compensating jet ...	57	57	57
Slow-running jet ...	50	50	50
Screw over capacity well ...	2.5 mm	2 mm	2 mm
Needle and seating ...	1.5 mm	1.5 mm	1.5 mm
Progression ...	—	100	—

Type (early A40, II)	SU H.S.2
Needle	M
Spring	Red

Type ('Sprite' I)	SU H.1 (two)
Needle (normal)	GG

Type ('Sprite' II and 'Midget' I, 948 cc)	SU H.S.2 (two)
Needle (Standard)	V3
Needle (Rich)	V2
Needle (Weak)	GX
Spring	Light blue

Type (A35 and A40, 1098 cc)	SU H.S.2
Needle (Standard)	AN
Needle (Rich)	H6
Needle (Weak)	EB
Spring	Red

Type (1098 cc 'Sprite' II and 'Midget' I)	SU H.S.2 (two)
Needle (Standard)	GY
Needle (Rich)	GG
Needle (Weak)	M
Spring	Blue

Type (1098 cc 'Sprite' III and 'Midget' II)	SU H.S.2 (two)
Needle (Standard)	AN
Needle (Rich)	GG
Needle (Weak)	H6
Spring	Blue

Fuel pump (all models except A40, II; 'Sprite' III and 'Midget' II)	AC 'Y' type (Mechanical)
A40, II ...	SU type S.P. (Electric)
'Sprite' III and 'Midget' II ...	SU type A.U.F. (Electric)

GEARBOX

Oil capacity (pints) ... $2\frac{1}{3}$

Gear ratios (overall):	First	Second	Third	Top	Reverse
A30 (up to chassis 1018) ...	19.94	12.63	8.19	5.143	25.25
A30 (after chassis 1018) ...	19.94	12.63	8.19	5.125	25.25
A30 (later) ...	19.94	12.63	8.19	4.875	25.25
A35 and 948 cc A40 ...	16.51	10.8	6.42	4.55	21.22
'Sprite' I ...	15.276	10.018	5.95	4.22	19.665
948 cc 'Sprite' II and 'Midget' I	13.504	8.085	5.726	4.22	17.361
1098 cc 'Sprites' and 'Midgets'	13.504	8.085	5.726	4.22	17.32
1098 cc A35 and A40 ...	15.276	9.169	5.95	4.22	19.665

BATTERY AND GENERATOR

Battery (positive earth):	Type (Lucas)	Normal capacity (amp/h)
A30 ...	GLTW 7A	30
A35 (early) ...	GTW 7A	38
A35 (later), A40, 948 cc 'Sprites' and 'Midgets'	BT 7A	43
1098 cc 'Sprites' and 'Midgets' ...	N9 or NZ9	

Generator type (Lucas):
    A30, A35 (early), A40, I (early) and 'Sprite' I C/39 PV2
    A35 (later), A40, I (later), and A40, II C/40–1
    948 cc 'Sprites' and 'Midgets' C/39
    1098 cc 'Sprites' and 'Midgets' C/40

Cut-out (all types):
    Cut-in voltage 12.7–13.3
    Drop-off voltage (RB 106/1)   9–10
    Drop-off voltage (RB 106/2) 8.5–11
Voltage regulator:
    Control box RB 106/1 used with early C/39 PV 2 generator
    Open-circuit setting at 3000 rev/min ...   ...   Voltage   Temp. correction (deg)

Voltage	C	F
16.1–16.7	10	50
15.8–16.4	20	68
15.6–16.2	30	86
15.3–15.9	40	104

    Control box RB 106/2 used with later C/39 and C/40 generators
    Open-circuit setting at 3000 rev/min ...   ...   Voltage   Temp. correction (deg)

Voltage	C	F
16.1–16.7	10	50
16.0–16.6	20	68
15.9–16.5	30	86
15.8–16.4	40	104

COOLING SYSTEM

Radiator capacity (pints):
    All models except 948 cc 'Sprites' and 'Midgets', ... $8\frac{1}{2}$
    948 cc 'Sprites' and 'Midgets'   10
    (Add one pint if heater fitted)

Thermostat opening temperature (deg):
    All 800 cc and 948 cc models except 'Sprite' II and 'Midget' I ...   70°–75°C
    948 cc 'Sprite' II and 'Midget' I   ...   .   65°–70°C
    1098 cc cars   ...   .   82°–83°C

FRONT SUSPENSION

Springs (free length):
    A30 and A35 ...   .   9.94
    A40   ...   .   10.04
    'Sprites' and 'Midgets' 9.4

STEERING

	A30, A35	A40	'Sprite' I	'Sprites' II and III 'Midgets' I and II
Castor angle (deg)	3	$3\frac{1}{2}$	3	3
Swivel pin inclination (deg) ...	$6\frac{1}{2}$	$6\frac{1}{2}$ (Mk I)	$6\frac{1}{2}$	$6\frac{3}{4}$
Camber angle (deg)	1	0	1	$\frac{3}{4}$
Toe-in (in)	$\frac{1}{16}-\frac{1}{8}$	$\frac{1}{8}-\frac{3}{16}$	$0-\frac{1}{8}$	$0-\frac{1}{8}$

Measured with the car in a static unladen condition

REAR AXLE

Oil capacity (pints)   ...   . $1\frac{3}{4}$

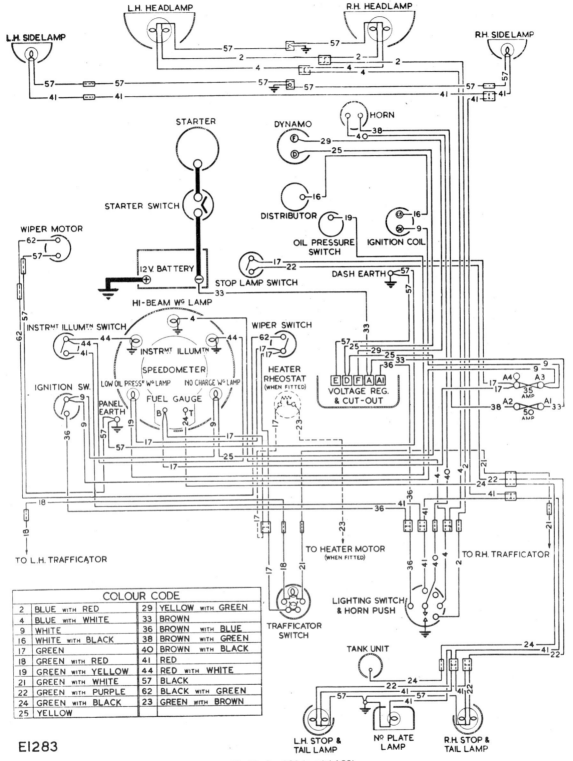

COLOUR CODE

2	BLUE with RED	29	YELLOW with GREEN
4	BLUE with WHITE	33	BROWN
9	WHITE	36	BROWN with BLUE
16	WHITE with BLACK	38	BROWN with GREEN
17	GREEN	40	BROWN with BLACK
18	GREEN with RED	41	RED
19	GREEN with YELLOW	44	RED with WHITE
21	GREEN with WHITE	57	BLACK
22	GREEN with PURPLE	62	BLACK with GREEN
24	GREEN with BLACK	23	GREEN with BROWN
25	YELLOW		

E1283

Fig 13 : A A30 (model AS3)

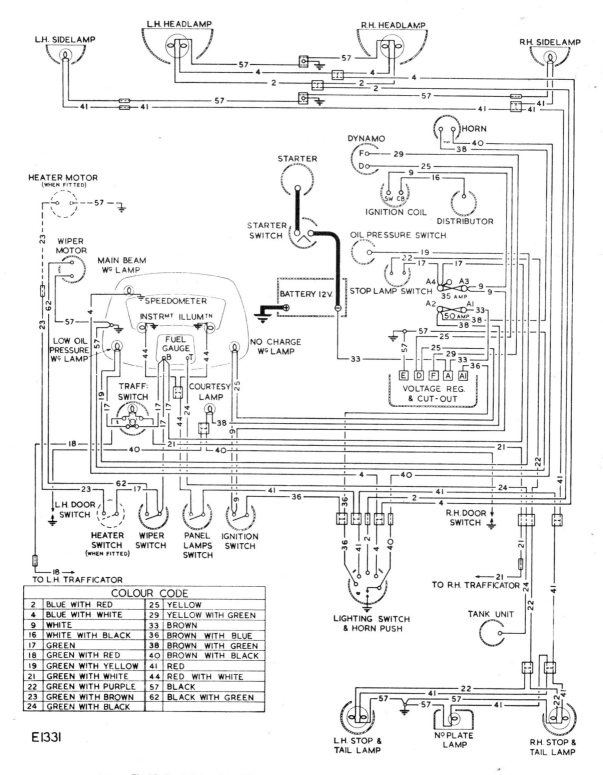

Fig 13 : B   A30 (models A2S4, AS4, AP4 and AV4). A35 (models AP5 and AV5)

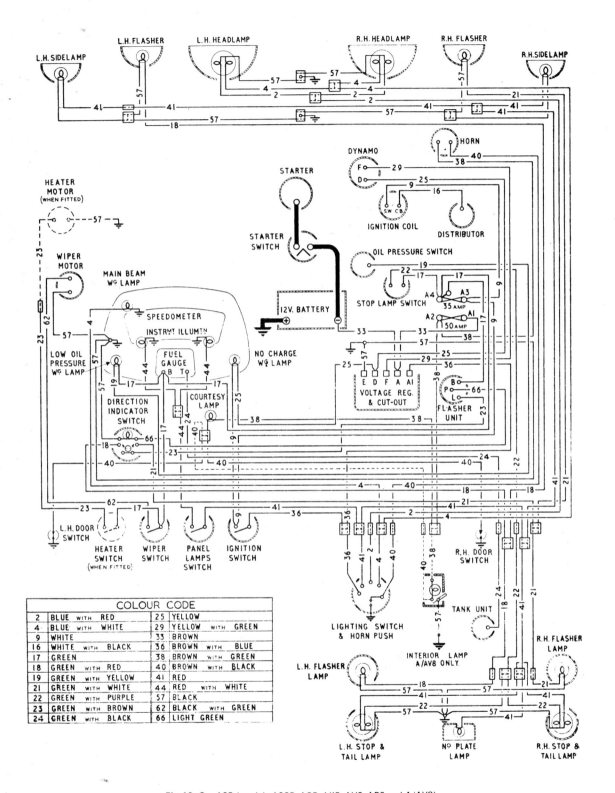

Fig 13: C A35 (models A2S5, AS5, AK5, AV6, AP6 and A/AV8)

COLOUR CODE				
2	BLUE WITH RED	25	YELLOW	
4	BLUE WITH WHITE	29	YELLOW WITH GREEN	
9	WHITE	33	BROWN	
16	WHITE WITH BLACK	36	BROWN WITH BLUE	
17	GREEN	38	BROWN WITH GREEN	
18	GREEN WITH RED	40	BROWN WITH BLACK	
19	GREEN WITH YELLOW	41	RED	
21	GREEN WITH WHITE	44	RED WITH WHITE	
22	GREEN WITH PURPLE	57	BLACK	
23	GREEN WITH BROWN	62	BLACK WITH GREEN	
24	GREEN WITH BLACK	66	LIGHT GREEN	

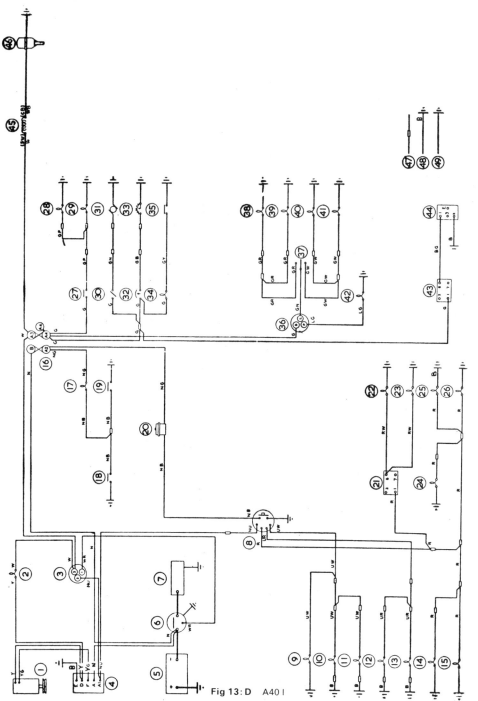

Key to Fig 13 : D   1 Dynamo.   2 Ignition warning light.   3 Ignition and starter switch.   4 Control box.   5 12-volt battery.
6 Starter solenoid switch.   7 Starter motor.   8 Lighting switch and horn push.   9 Main beam warning light.
10 R.H. headlamp main beam.   11 L.H. headlamp main beam.   12 L.H. headlamp dip beam.   13 R.H. headlamp dip beam.
14 L.H. sidelamp.   15 R.H. sidelamp.   16 Fuse unit.   17 Courtesy light.   18 Courtesy light switch.
19 Courtesy light switch.   20 Horn.   21 Panel light switch.   22 Panel light.   23 Panel light.   24 L.H. tail lamp.
25 Number plate lamp.   26 R.H. tail lamp.   27 Stop lamp.   28 L.H. stop lamp.   29 R.H. stop lamp.   30 Heater switch.
31 Heater motor.   32 Fuel gauge.   33 Fuel tank unit.   34 Oil pressure warning light.   35 Oil pressure warning light switch.
36 Flasher unit.   37 Flasher switch.   38 L.H. rear flasher.   39 L.H. front flasher.   40 R.H. front flasher.   41 R.H. rear flasher.
42 Flasher warning light.   43 Windshield wiper switch.   44 Windshield wiper switch motor.   45 Ignition coil.   46 Distributor.
47 Snap connectors.   48 Earth connections made via cable.   49 Via fixing bolts.

Cable Colour Code   B Black.   U Blue.   N Brown.   G Green.   P Purple.   R Red.   S Slate.   W White.   Y Yellow.
L Light.   D Dark.   M Medium.
When a cable has two colour code letters the first denotes the main colour and the second denotes the tracer colour.

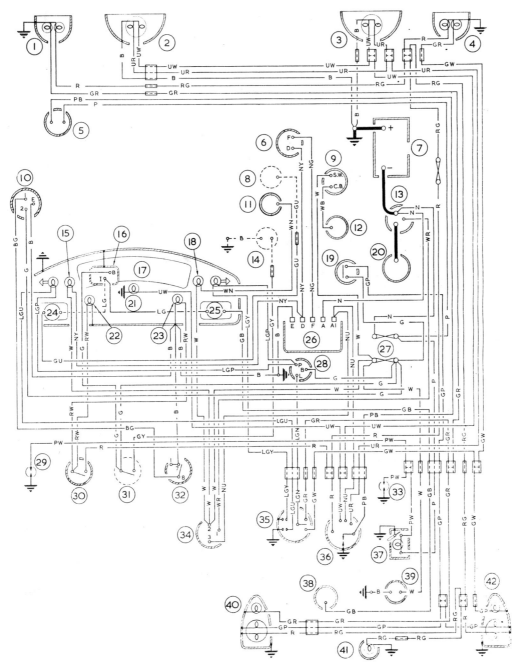

Fig 13 : E   A40 II

Key to Fig 13 : E   1 L.H. side and flasher lamp.   2 L.H. headlamp.   3 R.H. headlamp.   4 R.H. side and flasher lamp.   5 Horn
6 Dynamo.   7 Battery.   8 Thermometer element (when fitted).   9 Ignition coil.   10 Wiper motor.   11 Oil pressure switch
12 Distributor.   13 Starter solenoid.   14 Heater motor (when fitted).   15 Ignition warning lamp.   16 Regulator (10 volt)
17 Speedometer.   18 Low oil pressure warning lamp.   19 Stop lamp switch.   20 Starter.   21 Main beam warning lamp.
22 Panel light.   23 Panel light.   24 Thermometer gauge (when fitted).   25 Fuel gauge.   26 Control box.   27 Fuse unit.
28 Flasher unit.   29 Door switch.   30 Panel light switch.   31 Heater switch (when fitted).   32 Wiper motor switch.
33 Door switch.   34 Ignition and starter switch.   35 Flasher switch.   36 Lighting switch and horn push.   37 Interior light.
38 Tank unit.   39 Fuel pump.   40 L.H. stop/tail and flasher lamp.   41 Number-plate lamp.   42 R.H. stop/tail and flasher lamp.

Cable Colour Code   B Black.   U Blue.   N Brown.   G Green.   P Purple.   R Red.   S Slate.   W White.   Y Yellow.
L Light.   D Dark.   M Medium.
When a cable has two or three colour code letters the first or first two denote the main colour and the last the tracer colour.

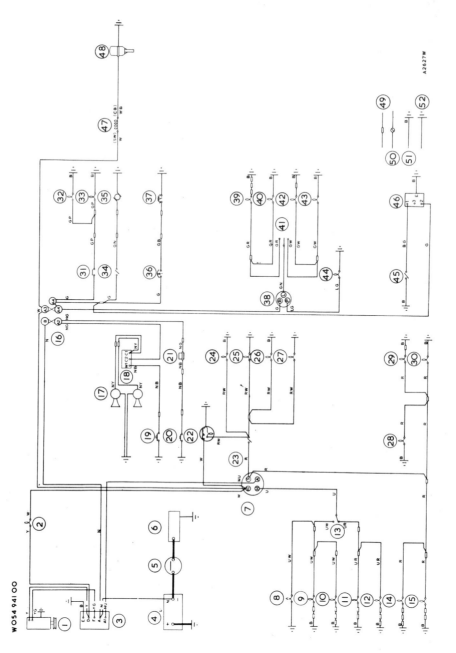

Fig 13: F 'Sprite' I

Key to Fig 13: F   1 Generator.   2 Ignition warning light.   3 Control box.   4 12-volt battery.   5 Starter switch.
6 Starter motor.   7 Lighting and ignition switch.   8 Main beam warning light.   9 R.H. headlamp main beam.
10 L.H. headlamp main beam.   11 L.H. headlamp dip beam.   12 R.H. headlamp dip beam.   13 Dipper switch.
14 L.H. sidelamp.   15 R.H. sidelamp.   16 Fuse unit.   17 Connections for twin windtone horns (when fitted).   18 Horn relay.
19 Horn push.   20 Horn push.   21 Horn.   22 Cigar lighter and illumination.   23 Panel light switch.   24 Panel light.
25 Speedometer light.   26 Panel light.   27 Tachometer light (when fitted).   28 R.H. tail lamp.   29 Number plate lamp.
30 L.H. tail lamp.   31 Stop lamp switch.   32 R.H. stop lamp.   33 L.H. stop lamp.   34 Heater switch (when fitted).
35 Heater motor (when fitted).   36 Fuel gauge.   37 Fuel gauge tank unit.   38 Flasher unit.   39 L.H. front flasher.
40 L.H. rear flasher.   41 Flasher switch.   42 R.H. rear flasher.   43 R.H. front flasher.   44 Flasher warning light.
45 Windshield switch.   46 Windshield wipers.   47 Ignition coil.   48 Distributor.   49 Snap connectors.
50 Terminal blocks or junction box.   51 Earth connections made via cable or   52 Via fixing bolts.

Cable Colour Code   B Black.   U Blue.   N Brown.   G Green.   P Purple.   R Red.   S Slate.   W White.   Y Yellow.
L Light.   D Dark.   M Medium.
When a cable has two colour code letters the first denotes the main colour and the second denotes the tracer colour.

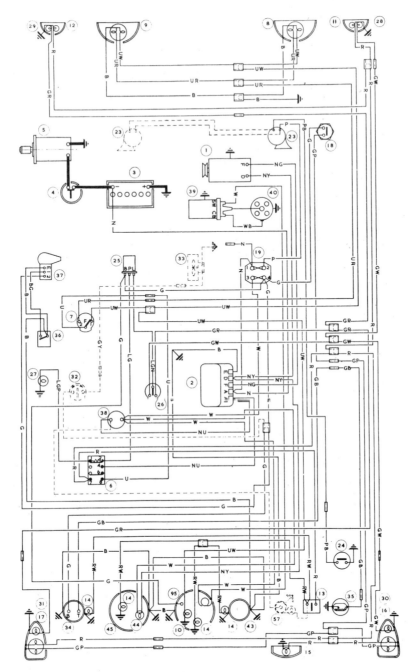

Fig 13 : G   'Sprite' II and 'Midget' I

Key to Fig 13 : G   1 Dynamo.   2 Control box.   3 Battery—12-volt.   4 Starter switch.   5 Starter motor.   6 Lighting switch.
7 Headlamp dip switch.   8 Headlamp—R.H.   9 Headlamp—L.H.   10 Main-beam warning lamp.   11 Sidelamp—R.H.
12 Sidelamp—L.H.   13 Panel lamps switch.   14 Panel lamps.   15 Number-plate illumination lamp.   16 Stop and tail lamp—R.H.
17 Stop and tail lamp—L.H.   18 Stop lamp switch.   19 Fuse unit.   23 Horn (twin horns when fitted).*   24 Horn-push.
25 Flasher unit.   26 Direction indicator switch.   27 Direction indicator warning lamp.   28 Front flasher lamp—R.H.
29 Front flasher lamp—L.H.   30 Rear flasher lamp—R.H.   31 Rear flasher lamp—L.H.   32 Heater or fresh-air motor switch.*
33 Heater or fresh-air motor.*   34 Fuel gauge.   35 Fuel gauge tank unit.   36 Windscreen wiper switch.
37 Windscreen wiper motor.   38 Ignition switch.   39 Ignition coil.   40 Distributor.   43 Oil pressure gauge.
44 Ignition warning lamp.   45 Speedometer.   57 Cigar-lighter.*   95 Tachometer (impulse) (later cars).
Note: All items marked (*) fitted as optional extras—circuits shown dotted.

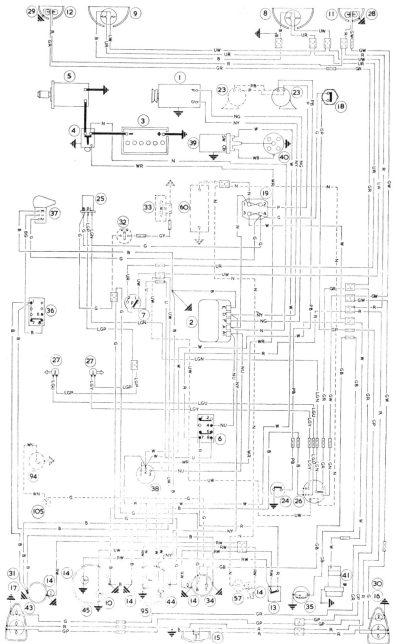

Fig 13:H 'Sprite' III and 'Midget' II

Key to Fig 13:H 1 Dynamo. 2 Control box. 3 Battery (12-volt). 4 Starter solenoid. 5 Starter motor. 6 Lighting switch. 7 Headlight dip switch. 8 R.H. headlamp. 9 L.H. headlamp. 10 Main-beam warning light. 11 R.H. sidelamp. 12 L.H. sidelamp. 13 Panel light switch. 14 Panel lights. 15 Number-plate illumination lamp. 16 R.H. stop and tail lamp. 17 L.H. stop and tail lamp. 18 Stop light switch. 19 Fuse unit (35 amps.). 23 Horn (twin horns when fitted). 24 Horn-push. 25 Flasher unit. 26 Direction indicator switch. 27 Direction indicator warning lights. 28 R.H. front flasher lamp. 29 L.H. front flasher lamp. 30 R.H. rear flasher lamp. 31 L.H. rear flasher lamp. 32 Heater or fresh-air motor switch (when fitted). 33 Heater or fresh-air motor (when fitted). 34 Fuel gauge. 35 Fuel gauge tank unit. 36 Windscreen wiper switch. 37 Windscreen wiper motor. 38 Ignition/starter switch. 39 Ignition coil. 40 Distributor. 41 Fuel pump. 43 Oil pressure gauge. 44 Ignition warning light. 45 Speedometer. 57 Cigar lighter (illuminated). 60 Radio. 94 Oil filter switch. 95 Tachometer. 105 Lubrication warning light.

Cable Colour Code N Brown. U Blue. R Red. P Purple. G Green. LG Light Green. W White. Y Yellow. B Black. When a cable has two colour code letters the first denotes the main colour and the second denotes the tracer colour.

INDEX

W